Math Innovations Course 1

MOVING MATH FORWARD THROUGH CRITICAL THINKING AND EXPLORATION

Notable Numbers

Focusing on Fractions, Decimals and Percents

Linda Jensen Sheffield

Suzanne H. Chapin

M. Katherine Gavin

You are one in a million

Kendall Hunt
publishing company

ACKNOWLEDGMENTS

Math Innovations Writing Team

Authors

Linda Jensen Sheffield

Suzanne H. Chapin

M. Katherine Gavin

Project Manager

Janice M. Vuolo

Teacher Edition Team

Alice J. Gabbard

Jennifer M. MacPherson

Ann Marie Spinelli

Writing Assistants

Jane Paulin

Jacob J. Whitmore

Kathy Dorkin

Mathematics Editor

Kathleen G. Snook

Assessment Specialist

Nancy Anderson

Advisory Board

Jerry P. Becker

Janet Beissinger

Diane J. Briars

Ann Lawrence

Ira J. Papick

Image on pg. 97 in public domain. All other images on cover and interior used under license by ShutterStock, Inc.

Kendall Hunt
publishing company

www.kendallhunt.com

Send all inquiries to:

4050 Westmark Drive

Dubuque, IA 52004-1840

1-800-542-6657

ISBN 978-0-7575-6685-1

Printed in the United States of America

4 5 6 7 8 9 10   14 13 12

Production Date: 11/28/12

Printed by: OneTouchPoint - CCI
Hartland, Wisconsin
United States of America

Batch number: 42668504

Notable Numbers:
Focusing on Fractions, Decimals and Percents
Table of Contents

UNIT GOALS

Notable Numbers: Focusing on Fractions, Decimals and Percents

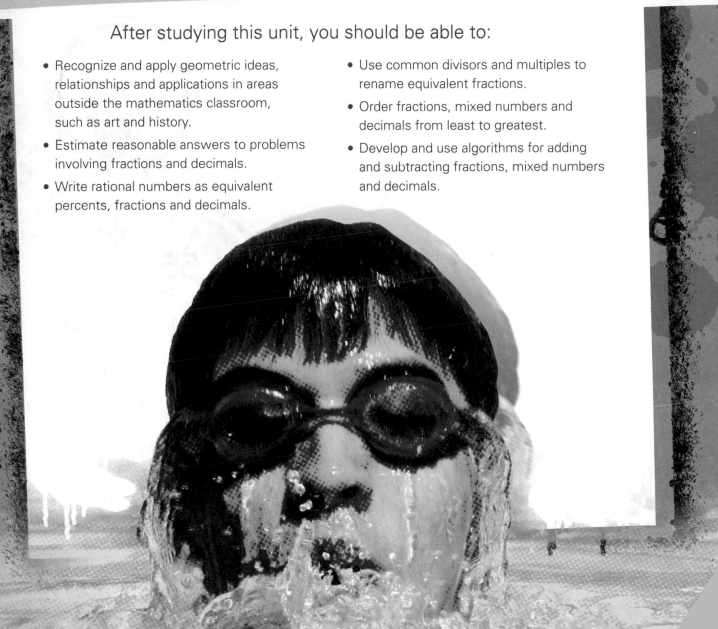

After studying this unit, you should be able to:

- Recognize and apply geometric ideas, relationships and applications in areas outside the mathematics classroom, such as art and history.

- Estimate reasonable answers to problems involving fractions and decimals.

- Write rational numbers as equivalent percents, fractions and decimals.

- Use common divisors and multiples to rename equivalent fractions.

- Order fractions, mixed numbers and decimals from least to greatest.

- Develop and use algorithms for adding and subtracting fractions, mixed numbers and decimals.

Dear Student Mathematician,

Did you know that people around the world did not use fractions or decimals for thousands of years? Just think about all the times you use fractions, decimals and percents. What types of problems couldn't you solve if you only used whole numbers?

Fractions, decimals and percents are rational numbers. In this unit, you will explore the historical development of rational numbers and deepen your own understanding of them. Throughout this unit, you will use several types of rational numbers to investigate a variety of problems and get a glimpse of just how much we depend on these numbers today.

We hope that you enjoy the activities and applications involving rational numbers in this unit. These explorations should help you build a strong foundation for your future work with these and other types of numbers.

Mathematically yours,
The Authors

Linda Sheffield

Suzanne H. Chapin

M. Katherine Gavin

SECTION 1

One Number, Many Names

You use whole numbers (0, 1, 2, 3, ...) to count and to solve many problems that use addition and multiplication. For other problems, you need fractions, decimals or mixed numbers. For example, the answer to $3 \div 5$ is not a whole number. You may write this quotient as 0.6 or $\frac{3}{5}$. The quotient of $3 \div 5$ is a rational number. Rational numbers are numbers that can be written as $\frac{a}{b}$, where a and b are integers, positive and negative whole numbers, but b is not equal to zero. All whole numbers are also rational numbers since any whole number a can be written as $\frac{a}{1}$. In this chapter we will use positive rational numbers.

MATHEMATICALLY SPEAKING

▶ whole number
▶ fraction
▶ decimal
▶ mixed number (or numeral)
▶ rational number
▶ integers
▶ percent
▶ equivalent fractions
▶ equivalent decimals

Over four thousand years ago the Babylonians used fractions. Their number system had a base of 60, instead of a base of ten like ours. This means they grouped numbers into sets of 60. Today we still use this base-60 system to measure time. The Chinese began to use a base-10 decimal system around 300 B.C. We use this same base-10 system today.

We can write each rational number as a fraction, decimal or percent. As a matter of fact, you will find that each rational number can be represented by an infinite number of equivalent fractions and equivalent decimals.

 LESSON 1.1

Understanding Percent

 Start It Off

List three things you know about percents. Discuss your list with a partner. Together, be prepared to discuss your list with the class.

Percents are used everywhere. For example, weather reports give the chance of rain as a percent. Many laptop computers and cell phones have displays that indicate the percent of the battery charge left. Where else have you encountered percents?

The word *percent* means "per one hundred." The concept of percent has been around for over 2,000 years. The Roman emperor Augustus made a tax called a *centesima*. The tax was 1 percent of the cost of each item sold at auction. That meant for every $100 worth of items sold, the tax was $1.

1. What would Romans owe in taxes for selling each of the following amounts?

   a) $200.00

   b) $500.00

   c) $1,500.00

   d) $150.00

2. Did you notice a pattern as you found 1% of each of these amounts? What happens to the decimal point?

3. How would you find 1% of numbers less than $100? What is 1% of $15 and 1% of $1.50?

Percent Strips

MATHEMATICALLY SPEAKING

▶ denominator
▶ numerator
▶ percent strip

Just as 100 cents is equal to 1 whole dollar (100¢ = $1.00), 100% is equivalent to 1 whole $\left(100\% = 1.00 = \frac{100}{100}\right)$. Note how the percent symbol (%) looks like a fraction bar. You can think of writing a fraction with a denominator of a hundred instead of using a percent symbol. For example, $15\% = \frac{15}{100}$ and $2\% = \frac{2}{100}$.

If a fraction has a denominator of 100 it is easy to convert it to a percent. The percent is the number in the numerator. For example, $\frac{25}{100} = 25\%$. In this activity, you will use a percent strip to investigate other fraction-decimal equivalents.

0%   100%

4. a) Cut out your percent strip and fold it in half so the 100% falls on the 0%. What percent is equal to $\frac{1}{2}$ of the strip? How do you know?

MATHEMATICALLY SPEAKING

▶ divisor

▶ factor (of a number)

▶ multiple

 Let's Review If a counting number, a, divides evenly into another number, b, with no remainder, that counting number, a, is a **divisor** or **factor** of the other number, b. The other number, b, is a **multiple** of the counting number, a.

b) How can you use the strip to find the percent equal to $\frac{1}{4}$? What about $\frac{1}{8}$? Is it easier to find a percent equal to a fraction if the denominator of the fraction is a divisor of 100?

c) You now know the percent that is equal to $\frac{1}{4}$. How would you find the percent equal to $\frac{2}{4}$? What about $\frac{3}{4}$?

d) Copy the chart below. Before folding the strip, record predictions for the percents equivalent to the fractions in the chart. Then fold the strip to locate each of the fractions. Label the strip with the fraction names and then record the percent equivalents in the chart. How close were your predictions?

Fraction of the Strip	Predicted Percent	Actual Percent
$\frac{1}{2}$		50%
$\frac{2}{2}$		
$\frac{1}{4}$		
$\frac{2}{4}$		
$\frac{3}{4}$		
$\frac{4}{4}$		
$\frac{1}{8}$		
$\frac{2}{8}$		
$\frac{3}{8}$		
$\frac{4}{8}$		
$\frac{5}{8}$		
$\frac{6}{8}$		
$\frac{7}{8}$		
$\frac{8}{8}$		

e) Do any of the fractions in the chart have the same value? Explain.

5. a) How does $\frac{1}{8}$ compare to $\frac{1}{4}$?

b) Robin said that $\frac{1}{8}$ looked like it was equal to 12%. Doug said he thought it looked more like 13%. Discuss with your partner the exact percent value for $\frac{1}{8}$. Explain your reasoning.

c) How could you find the percent equivalent to $\frac{3}{8}$? What about $\frac{5}{8}$?

6. Moesha said she could find all the fifths on her percent strip.

a) Predict the percents equal to $\frac{1}{5}$, $\frac{2}{5}$, $\frac{3}{5}$, $\frac{4}{5}$, and $\frac{5}{5}$. Take a new percent strip and fold it in fifths. Label each of the fifths on this strip. Were your predictions correct?

b) Talk to a partner about where the tenths will be on your strip. Fold your strip to check. Label tenths on the strip.

Think Beyond

c) If you have any number of fifths less than or equal to five, give an explicit rule for finding the equivalent percent. Use f to indicate the number of fifths?

Think Beyond

d) Write an explicit rule to find the percent that is equal to any number of tenths. Define your variable.

7. Anika said tenths, twentieths and hundredths were easier than other fractions to name as percents.

a) Name all the percents for each tenth from $\frac{0}{10}$ through $\frac{10}{10}$.

b) How might you use what you know about tenths to find percents that are equal to twentieths?

c) What percent is equal to $\frac{3}{10} + \frac{1}{20}$?

d) What percent is equal to $\frac{47}{100}$? How would you find the percent that is equal to any number of hundredths?

Hint
See page 150

Think Beyond

e) For each fraction, give an explicit rule to find the equivalent percent.

i) any number of eighths

ii) any number of twentieths

iii) any number of fourths

8. Use a new percent strip and predict the value of one-third as a percent. Fold the strip and mark it to show thirds.

a) Explain to a partner what percent is equivalent to $\frac{1}{3}$.

b) How might you use the percent equal to $\frac{1}{3}$ to find the percent that is equal to $\frac{2}{3}$?

c) How might you use the percent equal to $\frac{1}{3}$ to find the percent is equal to $\frac{1}{6}$? What about $\frac{2}{6}$? What about $\frac{1}{2}$?

 **W**rap It Up

We can use different fractions or a percent to name the same part of one whole. Give a few examples of this. Explain why the same part of one whole can have several different names.

MATHEMATICALLY SPEAKING

- ▶ decimal
- ▶ denominator
- ▶ divisor
- ▶ equivalent decimals
- ▶ equivalent fractions
- ▶ factor (of a number)
- ▶ fraction
- ▶ integers
- ▶ mixed number (or numeral)
- ▶ multiple
- ▶ numerator
- ▶ percent
- ▶ percent strip
- ▶ rational number
- ▶ whole number

 **Write About It**

For Questions 1–5, you may use the percent strips you made in the lesson.

1. Tanya knows that $\frac{1}{2} = 50\%$. Explain how she might use this information to find the percent equivalent to any number of fourths or eighths.

2. Copy and complete the following chart to show equivalent fractions and percents.

Fraction of the Strip	Percent
	$33\frac{1}{3}\%$
$\frac{3}{4}$	
	40%
$\frac{3}{8}$	
$\frac{9}{10}$	
	25%
$\frac{4}{4}$	
$\frac{7}{20}$	
	$62\frac{1}{2}\%$
$\frac{4}{5}$	

3. For each of the following, name two different equivalent fractions.

   a) 75%

   b) 20%

   c) 60%

4. Consider the following fractions.

   $\frac{3}{5}$ $\qquad$ $\frac{3}{8}$ $\qquad$ $\frac{3}{10}$ $\qquad$ $\frac{3}{4}$

   a) Convert each fraction to a percent. Order the percents from the least to the greatest.

   b) What do you notice about the numerators of each of the fractions? How might you use the denominators to order the fractions from the least to the greatest? How does the order compare to the order of the percents?

5. Name a fraction and the percent represented by each labeled point.

Point	Fraction	Percent
A		
B		
C		
D		
E		

6. On a recent test, 38% of the 13-year-old students in the United States said that $\frac{1}{5}$ is the same as 50%. Were they correct? Explain.

7. Jim said that $\frac{1}{5}$ is greater than $\frac{1}{4}$ because 5 is greater than 4. Is Jim correct? Explain.

8. Complete the chart for the quilt below.

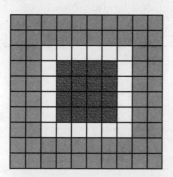

Color	Fraction	Percent
Green ▨		
Yellow ☐		
Blue ▦		
Total		

9. Use what you know about thirds to find the percent equivalents for sixths. Explain your method.

10. Claire said that $\frac{1}{2}\% = 50\%$. Explain to Claire why this is wrong. Include how $\frac{1}{2}\%$ can be written as a fraction and as a decimal.

Think Back

11. Write each of the following in words. Do not use the word *and* unless there is a decimal point or a mixed number.

   a) 845,005

   b) 987,923,481

   c) $\frac{4}{10}$

   d) $35\frac{4}{7}$

   e) $8,973\frac{23}{100}$

   f) 98,764.2

12. Which of the following is not a factor of 24?

   A. 2

   B. 10

   C. 12

   D. 8

13. What must be added to the product of 256 and 14 to make 15,000?

   A. 3,584

   B. 11,316

   C. 11,416

   D. 1,416

14. What is 232 ÷ 16?

   a) Write your answer with a remainder.

   b) Write your answer using a decimal.

15. What is $7 + 3 \cdot 4 - 2 \div 2$?

   A. 18

   B. 19

   C. 39

   D. 12

Percents in a Circle

Start It Off

On dot paper, divide the following squares into fourths in as many ways as you can. Each fourth must have the same area, but they do not need to be congruent. Two examples are shown below.

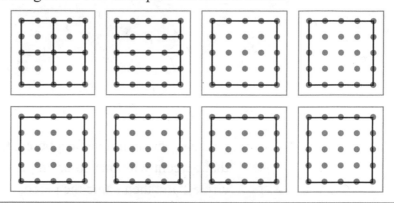

Percent Circles

A percent circle can be used to divide a circular region into parts to represent different percents. The whole circle represents 100%. Make a tool to help with finding percents by cutting two percent circles out of two different colors of sturdy paper. Cut each one on the radius that is marked by a dashed line. Slide the two circles together.

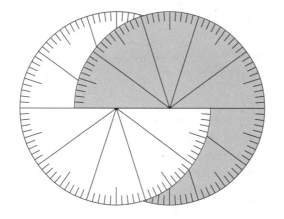 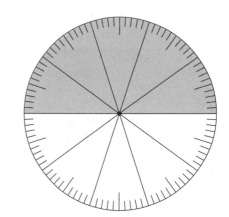

1. Look at the percent circle below.

   a) What percent is shaded on this percent circle? What percent is not shaded? What is the sum of these two percents?

   b) Write each of the percents from Part a as a fraction.

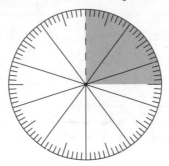

2. Work with a partner.

   a) One partner should name a percent. The other partner should show that percent with one color on the percent circle by turning the circles, and then name the percent shown by the other color. What is the sum of the two percents? Name each amount as a fraction. What do you notice?

   b) Trade roles with your partner and repeat Part a.

Use the percent circles to play the **What Percent?** game with your class.

G A M E · · · · · **What Percent?** · · · · ·

Players: whole class
Materials: percent circles
        What Percent? record sheet
        Questions for What Percent? game

DIRECTIONS:

To start the game, one person is chosen to be the leader. The leader will read a question about percents. Each player should record his or her prediction as a percent on the What Percent? record sheet. The leader will then give the players the answer as a fraction. Each player should rewrite the fraction as a percent. The score for the round is the difference between each player's prediction and the actual number written as a percent. The player with the lowest total wins.

Circle Graphs and Pie Charts

MATHEMATICALLY SPEAKING

▶ circle graph

▶ pie chart

Circle graphs, or pie charts, are used to show how a whole is divided into non-overlapping parts or categories. Jake did some research on Internet search engines and found the following chart:

Top U. S. Search Providers, Ranked by Searches, May 2007	
Provider	Share of Searches
Google	56%
Yahoo	22%
Windows Live	9%
AOL	5%
Ask.com	2%
Other	6%

Source: Nielsen//NetRatings, 2007

Jake said he could use his percent strip to make a circle graph of these data. First, he shaded his strip to show the percent for each provider. He shaded 56% of the strip light blue for Google, 22% red for Yahoo, 9% tan for Windows Live, 5% green for AOL, 2% royal blue for Ask.com and 6% brown for Other. He then wrapped the strip around a circle and shaded the circle to match his strip.

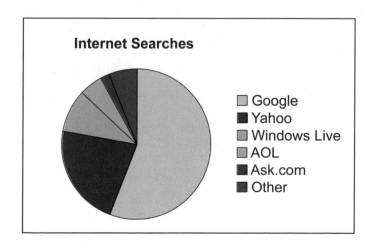

3. a) Make a circle graph to show the following information. Include the title, labels and percents on the graph.

Top U. S. Search Providers, Ranked by Searches, May 2008	
Provider	Share of Searches
Google	59%
Yahoo	18%
Windows Live (MSN)	12%
AOL	4%
Ask.com	2%
Other	5%

Source: Nielsen//NetRatings, 2008

b) How does your graph compare to Jake's? Is it easier to compare using the table or the circle graph?

c) Is it easier to compare the popularity of the search engines by using a table or a circle graph?

4. Erin found that in 2000, there were about a million students in Kentucky schools. About 12% were in nursery school; about 68% were in elementary, middle or high school; and about 20% were in college or graduate school. (factfinder.census.gov)

a) Make a circle graph that shows Erin's findings. Be sure to include a title, labels and percents on your graph.

b) What fraction of all the students were in college?

c) If there were a million students in school, about how many were in nursery school? What fraction of all the students is this?

Think Beyond

5. Now it is your turn to do some research. In a small group, make up a question of interest to your group. It might be students' least favorite food, how students get to school or some other question.

a) List four or five choices that answer your question. You will probably need to include "other" as a choice.

b) Ask 20 people to answer your question and record their answers.

c) Record the percent of people who gave each answer.

d) Create a circle graph to show the results.

e) Share your results with the class.

Think Beyond

f) If your survey is about a community issue ask more people to complete your survey. Then share your survey with the appropriate town or community group.

Wrap It Up

You have a circle graph with four sections. You know the percent for three of the sections. Describe how you would find the percent for the fourth section.

▶ circle graph

▶ percent circle

▶ pie chart

MATERIALS LIST

▶ Lesson Guide 2.1:
  On Your Own

▶ Pie chart circles

▶ percent strips

Write About It

1. How is a circle graph or pie chart similar to a percent circle? How is it different?

2. This pie chart shows the part of a pizza that is made up of each ingredient.

   a) What percent of the total pizza is made up of each ingredient?

   b) What is the total percent for all the ingredients?

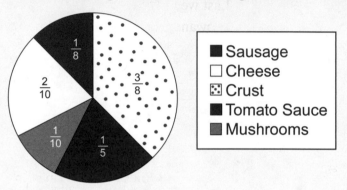

3. This pie chart shows the ingredients in another pizza. List the fractional part of the pizza that is made up of each ingredient.

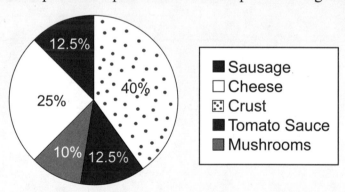

4. In 1 month, a car dealership sold 10 sport utility vehicles, 24 coupes, 50 minivans and 16 trucks.

   a) How many vehicles did the dealership sell in all?

   b) Find the fraction and percent of the total sales for each type of vehicle.

   c) Show this information in a pie chart. Be sure to include the title, labels and percents.

d) Another dealership sold 5 sport utility vehicles, 12 coupes, 25 minivans, and 8 trucks during the same month. The owner said that the minivans were 25% of the vehicles sold for the month. Was he correct? Make a pie chart showing the sales for this dealership. Compare it to the one that you drew in Part c.

5. Look up data (or survey 10 or 20 friends) on a topic you choose. Record your data in a table. Make a circle graph to show what you have found. Be sure to include the title, labels and percents for each section.

6. Todd's allowance is $10 per week. Maureen's allowance is $5 per week. Last week Todd saved 25% of his allowance. Maureen saved 50% of her allowance. Who saved more money? Explain.

7. a) The following chart shows the results of a survey asking people their favorite flavor of ice cream. Copy and complete it.

Flavor	Percent of Responses
Chocolate	25%
Vanilla	15%
Mint Chocolate Chip	40%
Other	

b) Shade sections of a hundredths grid to show the choices of favorite ice cream favors. Be sure to include a key to your grid.

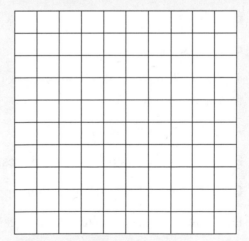

c) Make a pie chart to show the information. Include a title as well as a label and percent for each section.

d) How is shading the hundredths grid similar to making a pie chart? How is it different?

Think
Back

8. Write the following in numerals.

   a) two million five

   b) four and five-tenths

   c) sixty-two thousand and three-fourths

   d) four hundred six and two hundred forty ten-thousandths

9. Each section is what fraction of the total diagram?

   a)

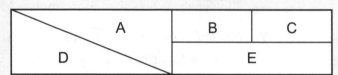

   b)

10. Tell whether each of the following is true or false for $x = 5$.

    a) $2x = 10$

    b) $7 - x = 2$

    c) $5x = 55$

11. There are 3 more apples than oranges in a bag. Which of the following might be true?

    A. There are 5 apples and 8 oranges.

    B. There are 12 apples and 9 oranges.

    C. There are 3 fewer oranges than apples.

12. Evaluate each of the following expressions for $n = 7$.

    a) $3n$

    b) $n + 8$

    c) $3n - 4$

LESSON 1.3 From Fractions and Percents to Decimals

 **Start It Off**

> You know that *percent* means "per hundred." In Latin, *cent* means one hundred. List three other words that contain *cent* that you think also may be related to the idea of one hundred. Give the definition of each. You may use a dictionary.

Markets and Decimals

MATHEMATICALLY SPEAKING

▶ unit fraction
▶ common fraction
▶ decimal place

In Europe during the Middle Ages, unit fractions (fractions with numerators of 1) and fractions with denominators of 60 were frequently used. Gradually, people began to use common fractions with any whole number numerator or denominator. In the 1500s, merchants began to use decimals to represent parts of a basic unit of money. Today we still use decimals for money. For amounts such as $3.98, the two decimal places show the cents portion (98¢) of the dollar amount.

1. Why do you think decimals are easier to use than common fractions for money?

2. Copy and complete the following chart to show the place value name, in words and as a power of 10, for each digit in the number 5,948,738,292. Read the number to a partner.

billions				ten thousands				tens	ones
10^9				10^5			10^2	10^1	1
5,	9	4	8,	7	3	8,	2	9	2

a) As you move from right to left, how many times greater is each place value?

b) What would you divide ten thousand by to get one thousand? What would you divide ten thousand by to get one hundred?

c) What is one divided by ten? How do you show this as a fraction? As a decimal?

d) What is one divided by one hundred? How do you show this as a fraction? As a decimal?

3. Copy and complete the following chart to show the place value name for each digit in the number 647.2358. Read the number to a partner. Be sure to read the decimal point as "and." Do not say "point two three five eight."

		ones	•		hundredths		
6	4	7	•	2	3	5	8

a) Using the digits 2, 3, 4, 5, 6, 7 and 8 each once, write the largest number you can that is less than 900. Read the number to your partner.

b) Using the digits 2, 3, 4, 5, 6, 7 and 8 each once, write the smallest number you can that is more than 200. Read the number to your partner.

 · · · · · **Wipeout** · · · · ·

Players: pairs

Materials: calculators (one per pair)

DIRECTIONS:

Put any number less than 100,000 in your calculator. You may use up to four decimal places. Challenge your partner to **Wipeout** one of the digits by making a zero appear in that place. Your partner should tell you the amount that he or she will subtract from your number to **Wipeout** the digit. and then check by doing the subtraction on the calculator. It is then your partner's turn to challenge you to **Wipeout** one of the digits left. Game ends when the calculator displays only a zero.

For example, you might put [54,908.3162] in the calculator. Then you could challenge your partner to **Wipeout** the 6. Your partner should then say, "I must subtract 6 thousandths." He or she should then push – [.006] on the calculator. Your partner might then challenge you to **Wipeout** the 5. After a few games, you might use larger numbers or more decimal places.

Making Sense of Cents, Decimals and Percents

Since *cent* means one hundred in Latin, it is not surprising that a cent is $\frac{1}{100}$, or 1%, of a dollar. Thirty-five cents can be written as $0.35. The two decimal places show cents to mean hundredths of a dollar. $0.35 is $\frac{35}{100}$, or 35%, of 1 dollar. Thirty-five hundredths is written as 0.35. The 3 is in the tenths place and the 5 is in the hundredths place. The zero before the decimal point shows that there is no whole number part of this decimal.

4. The entire diagram below represents 1 dollar.

a) How many of the smallest squares are in this dollar? Does one small square stand for an amount less than, equal to or greater than a penny?

b) What portion of the diagram is shaded? Give your answer in tenths, in hundredths and in thousandths.

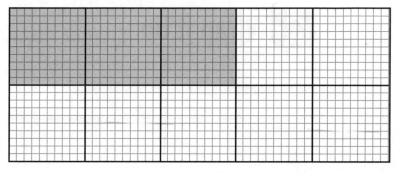

c) How many dimes are represented by the shaded portion? How many pennies?

d) Explain how you know that 0.3, 0.30 and 0.300 are equivalent.

5. Copy and complete the chart with equivalent amounts written as money, percents, fractions with a denominator of 100 and decimals.

Amount	Percent of a Dollar	Decimal Part of a Dollar	Fractional Part of a Dollar (with denominator of 100)
$0.80			
	8%		
			$\frac{6}{100}$
$0.02			
		0.2	

⬆W rap It Up_____

Explain how place value for whole numbers is similar to place value for decimals less than one.

LESSON
1.3 **SECTION 1**

On Your Own

MATERIALS LIST

▶ Lesson Guide 1.3:
   On Your Own

 **Write About It**

1. Choose a percent other than 50%. How can you write your percent in different ways using fractions and decimals? Use a percent circle, hundredths grid and/or percent strip in your explanation.

2. Mel had 85% of a dollar. He spent $\frac{3}{4}$ of a dollar for an apple. He then found $0.10. How much money does Mel have now?

3. The menu said hamburgers were .89¢. Liz ordered a hamburger and handed the clerk a penny. She told the clerk to keep the change. What was Liz thinking? Was she correct?

4. Write the fraction, decimal and percent for each labeled point on the percent strip.

Point	Fraction	Decimal	Percent
A			
B			
C			
D			
E			

5. A calculator shows the number 4,289.3156. What would you say, and what would you put into the calculator to "wipe out" the following:

   a) the 5

   b) the 3

   c) the 4

   d) the 6

6. Del said that 6% = 0.6. Serena said that 6% = 0.06. Who was right? Explain.

Think Back

7. Jan is 13. In five years, her grandmother will be four times as old as Jan will be then. How old is her grandmother now?

8. A troop of Boy Scouts sold 300 plants for $3 each. Using all the money from the sale, they bought 450 new plants. What was the cost of each new plant?

9. The sum of two consecutive whole numbers is 273. What is the least of the two numbers?

10. The sum of three consecutive whole numbers is 273. What is the greatest of the three numbers?

11. Approximate the fractional part of the circle shown by each lettered section.

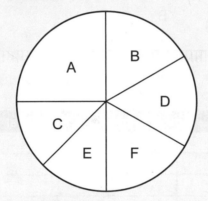

Decimals and the Metric System

**Start It Off**

> You may use a meterstick if you wish for these.
>
> 1. **a)**   1 meter = _____ centimeters   **b)**   10 centimeters = 1 _____
>
> 2. Find items in your classroom with approximately these measures:
>
>   **a)** 1.5 meters
>
>   **b)** 0.15 meter
>
>   **c)** 0.30 meter
>
>   **d)** 0.03 meter
>
> 3. **a)**   How many times larger is 1.5 meters than 0.15 meter?
>
>   **b)**   How many times larger is 0.30 meter than 0.03 meter?
>
>   **c)**   What patterns do you notice?

More Decimal Uses

MATHEMATICALLY SPEAKING

▶ meter

In the 1700s, the metric system was developed to simplify measurements. The creators of the metric system used units of ten. For example, a meter which is slightly longer than a yard, is a metric unit used to measure length. A decimeter (dm) is one-tenth (0.1) of a meter (m). A centimeter (cm) is one-hundredth (0.01) of a meter. A millimeter (mm) is one-thousandth (0.001) of a meter. The prefixes for metric measures (for example, deci, centi, and milli) are based on the place value chart we use for whole numbers and decimals. The following table compares the place value of numbers in the base-ten system to the prefixes for units of measure within the metric system.

Place Value of Amounts Larger Than a Unit			Unit	•	Place Value of Amounts Smaller Than a Unit		
thousands	hundreds	tens	ones	•	tenths	hundredths	thousandths
kilo (k)	hecto (h)	deka (da)	meter (m) liter (l) gram (g)	•	deci (d)	centi (c)	milli (m)
Metric Prefixes for Amounts Larger Than the Unit			**Metric Unit**		**Metric Prefixes for Amounts Smaller Than the Unit**		

A liter is used to measure volume and is an amount slightly more than a quart. A cup is about a fourth of a liter. A gram is used to measure mass.

1. Copy and fill in the blanks. Use decimal equivalents from the table. The first one is done for you. Note that just as 0.1 meter = 1 decimeter, 0.1 liter = 1 deciliter.

   a) 0.1 liter = 1 deciliter

   b) 10 liters = 1 _____

   c) 1 milliliter = _____ liter

   d) 250 milliliters = _____ liter

   e) 0.50 liter = _____ deciliters

2. Copy and fill in the blanks. Use a meter stick if you wish.

   a) Is your longest finger longer or shorter than a decimeter? Write 1 dm as a decimal part of a meter. 1 dm = _____ m

   b) Is the width of your pointer finger more or less than 1 cm? 1 cm = _____ m

   c) Is the width of the point of your pencil more or less than 1 mm? 1 mm = _____ m

GAME · · · · · Race to a Meter · · · · ·

Players: 2 (or 4 in two teams of 2)

Materials: one meterstick

two toothpicks of different colors or other small markers

Race to a Meter cards

DIRECTIONS:

Shuffle the Race to a Meter cards. Place them face down in a stack in the middle of the table. Choose your marker and put it at the zero on the meterstick. The goal is to be the first player to reach the end of the meter.

Player 1 should draw a card and move his or her marker the given distance. Player 2 should check that the move is correct. If so, the marker stays where it is, and it is Player 2's turn to draw a card and move. If the move is incorrect, the player must return the marker to the beginning and start over on the next turn. The first player to reach the end or beyond is the winner.

Wrap It Up

Explain how place value for whole numbers and decimals is related to the metric system.

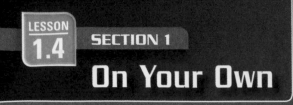
 **Write About It**

1. Explain how the prefixes *kilo, hecto, deka, deci, centi* and *milli* relate to place values in base ten.

2. Write each of the following lengths as a percent, a decimal and a fractional part of a meter.

Length	Percent of a Meter	Decimal Part of a Meter	Fractional Part of a Meter (with denominator of 100)
15 cm			
5 dm			
___ mm			$\frac{75}{100}$
___ dm	3%		
___ cm		0.2	

3. Name something in your home or school that is approximately each of the following lengths:

   a) 30% of a meter

   b) 0.05 m

   c) $\frac{3}{4}$ of a meter

   d) 0.2 m

4. Put a decimal point in the correct place to make each statement reasonable.

   a) Dwight, a tall sixth grader, is 187 meters tall.

   b) Sal drank 250 liters of orange juice for breakfast.

   c) Gas was $3,299 per gallon.

5. The following are heights of sixth grade students at Eastside Middle School.

Ming	162 cm	Maya	1 m and 30 cm	Anna	14.1 dm
Damien	179 cm	Will	17 dm	Kaye	15.7 dm

   a) Rewrite each height in meters. For example, 160 cm = 1.6 m or 1.60 m.

   b) Order the students from the shortest to the tallest.

Think Beyond

6. Which of the following have the same mass? Explain your thinking.

0.05 kilogram	500 decigrams	50 grams
50,000 milligrams	5 dekagrams	0.50 hectogram

Think Beyond

7. Chrissy ran 0.1 kilometer in 13.2 seconds. Sam ran 100 meters in 0.219 minute. Who was faster and by how many seconds?

Think Back

8. Fill in the blanks:

   a) 5 pints = ___ cups   **d)** 25 quarts = ___ gallons

   b) 3 miles = ___ feet   **e)** 50 ounces = ___ pounds

   c) 12 yards = ___ inches

9. A movie started at 2:45 pm and lasted for 105 minutes. What time did it end?

10. **a)** List all the factors of 30.

    b) List all the factors of 42.

    c) What is the greatest of the factors that 30 and 42 have in common?

11. **a)** List the first ten multiples of 4.

    b) List the first ten multiples of 3.

    c) What is the least of the multiples that 3 and 4 have in common?

12. Give the geometric name of each shape. In which section of the Venn diagram would you place each?

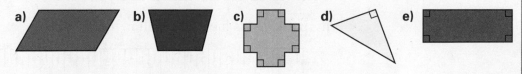

a)   b)   c)   d)   e)

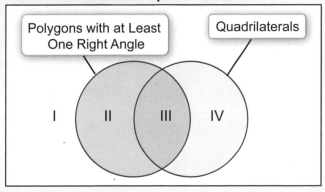

U = Geometric shapes

Polygons with at Least One Right Angle   Quadrilaterals

I   II   III   IV

Equivalent Fractions, Equivalent Decimals

Start It Off

1. **a)** Complete each factor tree to list all the prime factors of 24.

b) What do you notice about the prime factors? Do you get the same prime factors when you start with different factors?

2. **a)** Make three factors trees for 48. Start one with 3 • 16, one with 6 • 8 and the other with 4 • 12.

b) What do you notice about the prime factors at the end of each factor tree?

Measuring with Fractions and Decimals

Thomas Jefferson was the Secretary of State in 1789. He recommended weights and measures be based on powers of ten. When he was the President of the United States, he pushed for the country to use the metric system. Today, the United States is the only major country that still uses customary measurements of yards, inches, feet, miles, pints, quarts and pounds. This is one reason that fractions are very important.

1. Look at this inch ruler. Fill in the blanks.

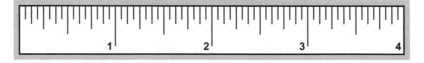

a) Each inch is divided into _____ equal intervals.

b) The length of each of the smallest intervals is _____ inch.

c) There are _____ of these smallest intervals in a half-inch.

2. **a)** Use a fraction or mixed number to name each labeled point on the following inch ruler.

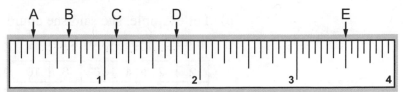

   b) Name the points on the following centimeter ruler using decimals.

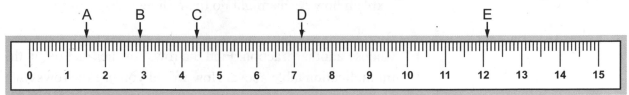

   c) Do you think it is easier to read a ruler in inches or in centimeters? Explain.

3. Bert and Ernie were discussing point A on the inch ruler below. Bert said that it was equal to $\frac{3}{4}$ inch. Ernie said it was $\frac{12}{16}$ inch.

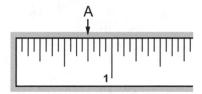

   a) Could both Bert and Ernie be correct? Explain.

   b) What is another fraction name for point A?

   c) List three different fractions to name point A. Explain how you found them. Are there other fractions for this point? How would you find them?

   d) Jasmine labeled point A as 0.12 inches. Was she right? Explain.

4. Aisha's little sister had to learn the multiplication facts on this table.

×	1	2	3	4	5	6	7	8	9	10	11	12
1	1	2	3	4	5	6	7	8	9	10	11	12
2	2	4	6	8	10	12	14	16	18	20	22	24
3	3	6	9	12	15	18	21	24	27	30	33	36
4	4	8	12	16	20	24	28	32	36	40	44	48
5	5	10	15	20	25	30	35	40	45	50	55	60
6	6	12	18	24	30	36	42	48	54	60	66	72
7	7	14	21	28	35	42	49	56	63	70	77	84
8	8	16	24	32	40	48	56	64	72	80	88	96
9	9	18	27	36	45	54	63	72	81	90	99	108
10	10	20	30	40	50	60	70	80	90	100	110	120
11	11	22	33	44	55	66	77	88	99	110	121	132
12	12	24	36	48	60	72	84	96	108	120	132	144

Aisha noticed that the numbers in any two rows of the table formed the numerators and denominators of equivalent fractions.

a) For example, she said she could use the two rows shown here to find fractions equivalent to $\frac{2}{3}$.

2	2	4	6	8	10	12	14	16	18	20	22	24
3	3	6	9	12	15	18	21	24	27	30	33	36

Explain how Aisha might do this? Draw a diagram to show why $\frac{2}{3} = \frac{6}{9}$.

b) Choose another fraction. Find the rows for the fraction on the multiplication table above. How would you use the rows to find equivalent fractions?

c) Find at least three fractions equivalent to each of the following:

i) $\frac{3}{4}$

ii) $\frac{4}{5}$

iii) $\frac{3}{8}$

iv) $\frac{5}{6}$

d) Explain to a partner why you can use the multiplication table to find equivalent fractions. Use a picture in your explanation. How many equivalent fractions can you find for a fraction using the multiplication table? Are there others?

MATHEMATICALLY SPEAKING

▶ common denominator

To determine which of two fractions is larger, it is often helpful to find a common denominator.

e) How would you use the multiplication table to find equivalent fractions with a common denominator for $\frac{5}{8}$ and $\frac{3}{4}$?

f) How would you use the multiplication table to find equivalent fractions with a common denominator for $\frac{4}{5}$ and $\frac{5}{6}$?

g) Name another pair of fractions with denominators less than 13. Challenge a partner to rename the fractions so they have a common denominator. Discuss your strategies.

Using Common Divisors and Common Multiples with Equivalent Fractions

MATHEMATICALLY SPEAKING

▶ algorithm
▶ least common multiple (LCM)
▶ greatest common divisor (GCD)
▶ least common denominator (LCD)

An algorithm is a step-by-step procedure for solving a problem. Around 2,000 years ago in China, scholars developed algorithms for renaming fractions. These algorithms used the least common multiple (LCM) and the greatest common divisor (GCD) of two numbers.

You can compare $\frac{4}{5}$ and $\frac{5}{6}$ without using the multiplication table. First, rename both fractions so that they have a common denominator. Then compare them.

5. **a)** List the first ten multiples of 5 and the first ten multiples of 6.

Find the smallest multiple that appears on both lists. This is called the least common multiple. For 5 and 6, the least common multiple is 30. That means that you could rename both $\frac{4}{5}$ and $\frac{5}{6}$ as fractions with a denominator of 30, the least common denominator (LCD).

    b) Rename $\frac{4}{5}$ and $\frac{5}{6}$ as fractions with denominators of 30. To this, multiply the numerator and denominator of each fraction by the same number. For example, $\frac{4}{5} = \frac{4 \cdot 6}{5 \cdot 6} = \frac{24}{30}$.

    c) Which is larger, $\frac{4}{5}$ or $\frac{5}{6}$? Explain.

    d) How does this method compare to using the multiplication table as you did for Question 4f?

    e) How would you compare $\frac{3}{4}$ and $\frac{2}{3}$? Which number is larger?

6. You can use the method of listing multiples to find common multiples of numbers that are not in the multiplication table. Think about the numbers 12 and 15.

    a) List the first ten multiples of 12 and the first ten multiples of 15.

    b) List two multiples of 12 and 15 that you find in both lists. Which of these is the least common multiple?

    c) How would you find the least common denominator for $\frac{5}{12}$ and $\frac{4}{15}$? Rewrite each fraction with this least common denominator and show your work.

7. **a)** List the first eight multiples of each number. Use the least common multiple to write the fractions given as equivalent fractions with a common denominator. Show your work. The first row has been done for you.

Numbers	First Eight Multiples	Fractions with the Least Common Denominator
10, 6	10, 20, 30, 40, 50, 60, 70, 80 6, 12, 18, 24, 30, 36, 42, 48	$\dfrac{7 \cdot 3}{10 \cdot 3} = \dfrac{21}{30}$ $\dfrac{5 \cdot 5}{6 \cdot 5} = \dfrac{25}{30}$
6, 4	6, 4,	$\dfrac{5}{6}$ $\dfrac{1}{4}$
3, 18	3, 18,	$\dfrac{2}{3}$ $\dfrac{7}{18}$
7, 5	7, 5,	$\dfrac{3}{7}$ $\dfrac{2}{5}$

b) Use a common denominator of 60 to decide if $\dfrac{7}{10}$ or $\dfrac{5}{6}$ is larger. Then do this with 30 as a common denominator. Do both methods give you the same answer?

c) Use a common denominator of 24 to decide if $\dfrac{5}{6}$ or $\dfrac{3}{4}$ is larger. Then do this with 12 as a common denominator. Which method do you prefer?

8. Abe said that there are many names for each point on a ruler. He said he always likes to use the simplest name possible. By "simplest," he means the name with the smallest whole number numerator and denominator.

a) List three names for each of the points shown on the ruler. Circle the simplest name in each list.

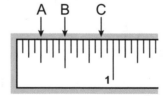

Abe said that when you divide the numerator and denominator by the same number, you don't change the value of the fraction. Abe first divides by the smallest common factor, and then checks to see if there is another factor he can divide by. For example, if you start with $\dfrac{12}{16}$ and divide both numbers by 2, you get $\dfrac{6}{8}$. Although $\dfrac{6}{8}$ is simpler than $\dfrac{12}{16}$, there is an even simpler fraction with the same value. You can divide both 6 and 8 by 2 and get $\dfrac{3}{4}$. All three fractions are equivalent: $\dfrac{12}{16} = \dfrac{6}{8} = \dfrac{3}{4}$.

$$\dfrac{12 \div 2}{16 \div 2} = \dfrac{6}{8}$$

$$\dfrac{6 \div 2}{8 \div 2} = \dfrac{3}{4}$$

b) Use Abe's method to simplify each of the following fractions. Stop when you can no longer divide the numerator and denominator evenly by the same number. Your fraction is then in simplest form. Show your work.

i) $\frac{8}{12}$

ii) $\frac{16}{40}$

iii) $\frac{14}{28}$

9. Marybeth found a way to use the greatest common divisor (GCD), or greatest common factor (GCF) to simplify a fraction. She said, "Suppose I want to simplify $\frac{24}{30}$. I know that 6 is the largest number that is a factor of both 24 and 30. I can divide both 24 and 30 by 6 to simplify $\frac{24}{30}$."

a) Simplify $\frac{24}{30}$ using Abe's method. Compare this to Marybeth's method. Which method do you prefer?

b) Simplify each of the following fractions. Show your work.

i) $\frac{18}{27}$

ii) $\frac{54}{81}$

iii) $\frac{32}{48}$

iv) $\frac{28}{42}$

 c) Some calculators have a "Simplify" button. If you have one on your calculator, use it to check your answers in Part b. Do the answers on the calculators match your answers from Part b? Explain.

Equivalent Decimals

There are an infinite number of equivalent fractions to name any given value. Decimals that have the same value are equivalent decimals. How many decimals do you think there are to name the same amount?

10. Manuel said that ten-hundredths (0.10) must be equivalent to one-tenth (0.1). He said this because ten pennies are equivalent to one dime. A dime is one-tenth (0.1) of a dollar and ten pennies are ten-hundredths (0.10) of a dollar. He wrote 0.1 = 0.10. Was he correct? Explain.

11. Look at a meterstick.

   a) Write a millimeter as a decimal part of a meter.

   b) Write a centimeter as a decimal part of a meter.

   c) How many millimeters are there in a centimeter? Show this using decimals.

MATHEMATICALLY
SPEAKING

▶ annex zero

12. Will said that finding equivalent decimals is easier than finding equivalent fractions. All you have to do is annex zeros to the far right of the decimal.

   a) How does this work? Is this the same as adding zero to the number?

   b) Why does this work?

   c) Use Will's method to complete the following table.

Tenths	Hundredths	Thousandths
0.4		
	0.50	
		0.200
	0.70	
0.3		

   d) Sally wants to write each decimal as a fraction with 10, 100 or 1,000 in the denominator. For example, she could write $0.7 = \frac{7 \cdot 10}{10 \cdot 10} = \frac{70}{100} = 0.70$. Choose two of the decimals on the chart. Show how you would rename these as equivalent decimals using Sally's method.

13. One way to convert a fraction to a decimal is to divide.
$\frac{3}{4} = 3 \div 4$

You could find the equivalent decimal by carrying out the division:
$$3 \div 4 = 4\overline{)3.00}\,.\ \ \ \ \ \ \overset{.75}{}$$

   a) Compare this to finding an equivalent fraction with a denominator that is a power of ten as in this example.
   $\frac{3 \cdot ?}{4 \cdot ?} = \frac{?}{100}$

   b) Find a decimal equivalent to each of the following fractions. Show your work.

   i) $\frac{4}{5}$

   ii) $\frac{5}{8}$

   iii) $\frac{3}{6}$

   iv) $\frac{7}{25}$

Wrap It Up

- How do you use common factors to simplify a fraction? How would you use the greatest common factor?

- How do you use common multiples to decide which of two fractions is greater? How would you use the least common multiple?

MATERIALS LIST

▶ Lesson Guide 1.5:
*Equivalent Fractions
and Decimals*

Write About It

1. Start with the fraction $\frac{16}{20}$.

   a) Find at least five fractions equivalent to this fraction.

   b) Find the simplest equivalent fraction. How can you find this fraction in one step?

   c) Rename the fraction $\frac{16}{20}$ with a denominator of 10. Then write this as a decimal. Find an equivalent fraction with a denominator of 100 and then 1,000. What do you notice?

   d) Write a rule for changing a fraction with a denominator of 10, 100 or 1,000 to a decimal.

2. **a)** List two equivalent fractions to name each point on the following inch ruler. Be sure to label each in inches.

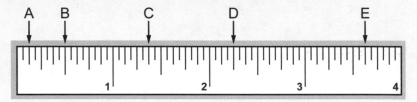

   b) List two decimals and one fraction in simplest form for each point on the following centimeter ruler. Be sure to label each point in centimeters.

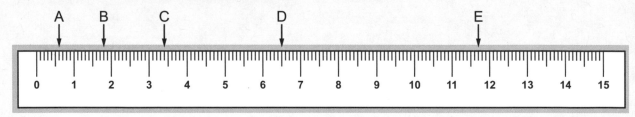

3. Find each point on the number line below and label it with the given letter. You should first find the value of each space on the number line.

   $A = \frac{5}{6}$ $B = 66\frac{2}{3}\%$ $C = 0.25$ $D = \frac{3}{9}$ $E = 1\frac{1}{2}$

4. A fraction bar can be thought of as a division sign. $\frac{5}{16}$ is the same as $5 \div 16$.

a) Write three equivalent fractions for $\frac{5}{16}$.

b) For each fraction in Part a, use your calculator to divide the numerator by the denominator. What do you notice?

c) Choose your own fraction. Do not use $\frac{1}{2}$. List three fractions that are equal to your fraction. For each of the fractions, divide the numerator by the denominator on your calculator. What do you notice about the decimals that are equal to equivalent fractions?

5. Fill in the missing parts to rewrite each of the following as an equivalent fraction.

a) $\frac{5}{12} = \frac{?}{24}$

b) $\frac{6}{9} = \frac{2}{?}$

c) $\frac{18}{12} = 1\frac{1}{?}$

d) $\frac{12}{?} = 2\frac{2}{5}$

6. It's easy to convert fractions with 100 as a denominator to percents.

a) Rename each of the following as fractions with a denominator of 100 and as a decimal. Then write each as a decimal and as a percent.

Original Fraction	Work	Fraction with a Denominator of 100	Decimal	Percent
$\frac{3}{4}$				
$\frac{7}{25}$				
$\frac{9}{20}$				
$\frac{3}{5}$				
$\frac{13}{50}$				

b) How are fractions with a denominator of one hundred, decimals and percents related?

7. Complete each of the following with a fraction in simplest form.

a) 12 inches = _____ yard

b) 8 ounces = _____ pound

c) 45 minutes = _____ hour

d) 24 minutes = _____ hour

e) 500 pounds = _____ ton

8. Hank said that you could just keep annexing zeros with decimals and the number would still be the same.

   a) Hank said that $0.4 = 0.40 = 0.400$. Was he correct? Explain.

   b) Greta said that $0.4 = 0.04 = 0.004$. Was she correct? Explain.

9. Highlands Middle School has a few after-school clubs.

   a) Copy and complete the table.

Club	Number of Boys	Number of Girls	Total Students
Spanish Club	12	4	
Computer Club	12		36
Glee Club		12	30
Drama Club	56	8	

   b) Copy and complete the following table. For each club, write the simplest fraction to show the portion of students in the club who are boys. Then write equivalent decimals and percents for each.

Club	Original Fraction	Simplest Fraction	Decimal	Percent
Spanish Club	$\frac{12}{16}$			
Computer Club				
Glee Club				
Drama Club				

   c) Write a rule for finding the simplest form of any fraction.

   d) How many fractions are equivalent to any given fraction? Explain.

   e) Which club has the greatest percent of boys?

Think Beyond

10. Copy the number line, locate each point and label it with the given letter.

   $A = \frac{3}{16}$ $B = 12\frac{1}{2}\%$ $C = 0.25$ $D = \frac{3}{8}$ $E = 1\frac{1}{4}$

   ← | | | | | | | | | | | | | | | | | | | | | | | | →
   0   75%

11. A two-gallon jug of lemonade costs $4.95. At the school fair, the lemonade was sold in eight-ounce glasses for $0.95 a glass. How much money did the school make for every 2 gallons of lemonade they sold?

Hint
See page 150

12. Zeke bought four books for $32.00. He then bought two more books for $5 apiece. What was the average cost of each of the six books?

13. True or false:

a) $7 \cdot \frac{56}{56} = 7 \div \frac{23}{23}$

b) $7 \cdot \frac{a}{a} = 7$ (*a* cannot be zero)

c) $7 + \frac{a}{a} = 7$ (*a* cannot be zero)

d) $7 + \frac{12}{12} = 7 + \frac{5}{5}$

e) $7 + \frac{12}{12} = 7 - \frac{5}{5}$

14. What is the product of 585 and 13?

A. 45

B. 7,505

C. 6,605

D. 7,605

Think Beyond

15. You have a blank ruler with no marks that is exactly 13 cm long. You can put four marks on it. You want to be able to measure all centimeter values from 1 to 13 cm. You may not use any measure more than once to get the same centimeter value. For example, you could measure 3 cm by using measures for 1 cm and 2 cm. However, you could not use the 1 cm measure three times. Where should you put the four marks?

Measure That

LESSON 1.6

➡ Start It Off

Fill in the blanks:

1. $2{,}000 \div 10 =$ ___

2. $200 \div 10 =$ ___

3. $20 \div 10 =$ ___

4. $2 \div 10 =$ ___

5. $0.2 \div 10 =$ ___

6. What pattern do you notice?

7. List the next two division problems in this pattern.

More Than One

MATHEMATICALLY SPEAKING

▶ improper fraction
▶ proper fraction

Fractions can be written in the form $\frac{a}{b}$. If a is greater than or equal to b, then $\frac{a}{b}$ is an **improper fraction**. If a is less than b, then $\frac{a}{b}$ is a **proper fraction**. JoRae said you could write any improper fraction as a whole number or mixed number. She said this tells you the number of wholes in the fraction. For example, take the fraction $\frac{11}{6}$. JoRae knows that $\frac{6}{6} = 1$. After she takes $\frac{6}{6}$ from $\frac{11}{6}$, she has $\frac{5}{6}$ left. She then writes $\frac{11}{6} = \frac{6}{6} + \frac{5}{6} = 1\frac{5}{6}$.

JoRae used pattern blocks to show this pattern. She said that each hexagon represents a whole, or 1. Each triangle is $\frac{1}{6}$ of the whole because it takes six triangles to form one hexagon. Eleven triangles (which represent $\frac{11}{6}$) make one hexagon and $\frac{5}{6}$ of another.

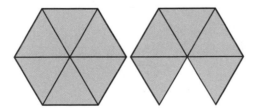

1. Write the improper fractions as mixed numbers in simplest form. Show your work. The first is done for you.

   a) $\frac{10}{4} = \frac{4}{4} + \frac{4}{4} + \frac{2}{4} = 2\frac{2}{4} = 2\frac{1}{2}$

   b) $\frac{8}{5}$

   c) $\frac{24}{9}$

   d) $\frac{14}{6}$

   e) $\frac{10}{8}$

Sticks and Tape

LeBraun wanted to measure the size of the horse stalls in a barn. He found an old broken yardstick where only the $\frac{2}{3}$ yd. mark was showing. He also found a roll of adding machine tape. LeBraun then decided that he could still use the yardstick to do all his measuring.

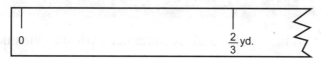

For this activity you need a strip of adding machine tape, some transparent tape and several crayons.

2. Work with two other students. You should each have a length of adding machine tape that is $\frac{2}{3}$ yard long. You will use these to make a measuring tape. Put a zero on the left-hand side and $\frac{2}{3}$ on the right-hand side. Mark each length below on your tape. Use a different color each time. You may fold your strip or tape strips together to help find some of the measures. Record a brief description of what you did so you can share this with the class.

   a) $\frac{1}{3}$ yard

   b) $\frac{1}{6}$ yard

   c) $\frac{1}{2}$ yard

   d) 25% of a yard

   e) 1 whole yard

3. Repeat this process for each of the following lengths.

    a) 1 yard

    b) 1.75 yards

    c) $\frac{11}{6}$ yards

4. **a)** Mercedes started with 1 yard and added $\frac{1}{2}$ yard and $\frac{1}{3}$ yard. Her partner started with 2 yards and then subtracted $\frac{1}{6}$ yard. Did they find the same length? Explain.

    b) LeBraun said that he found $\frac{1}{12}$ yard. He started with a full strip and then folded it in half to find $\frac{1}{3}$ yard. He then folded this in half, and then folded it in half again. Meredith found $\frac{1}{12}$ yard by starting with a tape that was 25% of a yard. She then folded it in thirds. Could they both be correct? Explain.

    c) Is there another way to find $\frac{1}{12}$? Explain.

Measuring Cups and Strips

Morgan found a glass container with straight sides that holds exactly $1\frac{1}{3}$ cups.

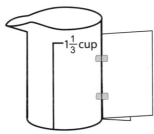

She wanted to measure the ingredients for cookies, but she had only the glass container. Morgan decided that she could use a strip of paper to find the other measurements. Her recipe calls for:

- $\frac{3}{2}$ cup quick-cooking oats
- $\frac{3}{4}$ cup all-purpose flour
- $\frac{3}{4}$ cup brown sugar
- $\frac{1}{2}$ cup vegetable shortening

5. Cut a strip of paper and mark one end 0 c and the other end $1\frac{1}{3}$ c.

    a) How would you find the mark for 1 cup?

    b) Why is it helpful to find 1 whole unit before marking other fractions of a cup?

    c) How would you mark the strip to find the other amounts that she needs for the recipe.

Wrap It Up

When you know an amount, such as $\frac{3}{4}$ cup, how can you find other measures, such as 1 cup? How would you find $\frac{9}{8}$ cup?

MATHEMATICALLY SPEAKING

▶ improper fraction

▶ proper fraction

 **Write About It**

1. The distance from Janelle's elbow to her wrist is $\frac{3}{4}$ foot. Explain how she might use this to measure $\frac{2}{3}$ or $\frac{7}{6}$ foot. How is it helpful to find the unit of 1 whole foot?

2. Copy the number line below and mark each letter on it. How did you find the right spot for each letter? You may use your ruler or adding machine tape.

   a) $A = \frac{2}{3}$

   b) $B = 25\%$ of a unit

   c) $C = 0.75$

   d) $D = \frac{13}{8}$

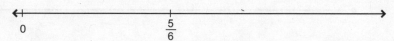

3. Sal wants to buy a picture frame for a photo that is $\frac{1}{3}$ foot by $\frac{1}{2}$ foot. He forgot to bring a measuring tape with him. He has his library card, which is $\frac{1}{6}$ foot wide. How might he use his card to measure the picture frame?

4. Danielle knows that a dollar bill is half a foot long. How could she use the dollar to measure a mat for her desk that should be $1\frac{2}{3}$ feet by $\frac{5}{4}$ feet?

5. Point A marks $\frac{1}{3}$ foot. Find the length from 0 to each letter. Write each as a fraction or mixed number in simplest form.

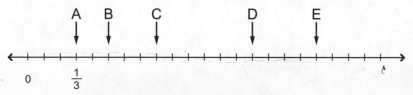

   The number line is not drawn to scale.

6   If possible, find one or more values for each of the variables to make each a true statement.

a) $\dfrac{5 + a}{8 + a} = \dfrac{5}{8}$

b) $\dfrac{5 - b}{8 - b} = \dfrac{5}{8}$

c) $\dfrac{5 \cdot c}{8 \cdot c} = \dfrac{5}{8}$

d) $\dfrac{5 \div d}{8 \div d} = \dfrac{5}{8}$

Think Beyond

7. Mr. Johnson has a bag of peanuts that weighs $1\frac{5}{8}$ pounds. He wants to give his neighbor exactly $\frac{3}{4}$ pound of peanuts. He has nothing to measure with. How might he find exactly $\frac{3}{4}$ pound?

Think Back

8. A bedroom floor is 12 feet by 15 feet. How many square feet is the bedroom floor?

9. Can an odd number have any even digits in it? If so, where must the even digits be placed? Explain.

10. Order from the least to the greatest.

    14,325   14,235   14,328   14,235.9

11. In a basketball game, the University of Kentucky was ahead of Michigan State, 82 to 75. After that, Michigan State scored 18 of the final 25 points. What was the final score?

12. Suppose your heart beats 70 times a minute. How many times will it beat in 3 hours?

13. Trace each of the following figures. Draw all their lines of symmetry.

  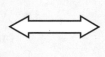

Putting It All Together

Start It Off

A star athlete says he always gives 110% in every game. Do you agree? Explain.

Batteries and Charges

On Tori's computer, a small image in the bottom right corner shows how much time is left on the battery. For example, when the image looks like 🔋, she knows that the battery is 75% charged. When the battery is fully charged, Tori can use it for four hours. She makes the following diagram.

0	_hour	_hours	_hours	4 hours
0	_%	_%	_%	100%

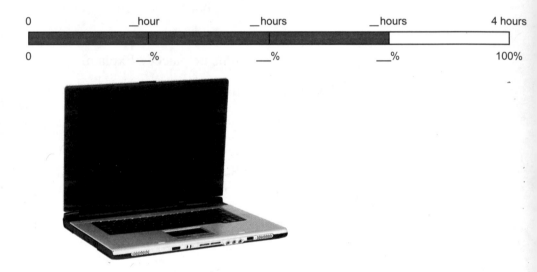

1. a) Copy the diagram. Fill in the missing numbers of hours and percents.

b) What percent charge is left on the battery? How much time is left on the battery? Explain.

2. a) Draw a diagram to show Tori's battery with a 20% charge.

b) How long will her battery last if it has a 20% charge? Give your answer as a fractional part of an hour.

c) Give your answer in minutes.

3. a) Draw a diagram that shows Tori's battery with only a half hour left on the charge.

b) What percent of the charge on the battery is left?

c) What fraction of a full charge is left?

Fill It Up

Jake can tell how much gas is left in his car by estimating the percent on the gas gauge.

Jake drew the diagram to show the gas gauge. Use this diagram to answer Questions 4–8.

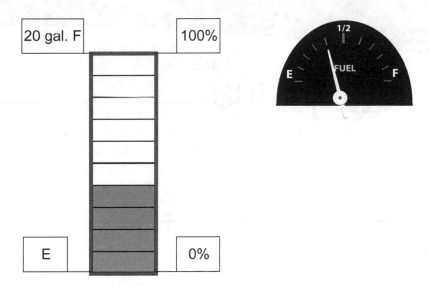

4. a) What percent of the tank was full?

b) What fraction of the tank is this?

5. A full tank holds 20 gallons. How many gallons are in the tank now?

6. Copy Jake's diagram. Label the diagram to show the level of gas for each of the following.

    a) 25% full = _____ gallons

    b) _____ % full = 1 gallon

    c) 75% full = _____ gallons

    d) 10% full = _____ gallons

    e) _____ % full = 10 gallons

    f) 40% full = _____ gallons

7. Eli found the percent for 1 gallon. He then found the other amounts. How would Eli find the percent of the tank that is full if there are 7 gallons in the tank?

8. Angie found the number of gallons in 10% of the tank. She then found the other amounts. How would Angie find the number of gallons in 60% of the tank?

Wrap It Up

When working with percents, it is important to know the value of 100% or 1 whole. Battery 1 has a 100% charge that can be used for 3 hours. Battery 2 has a 75% charge that can be used for 3 hours. How would you find the number of hours left on each battery when they have a 50% charge?

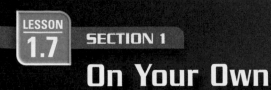
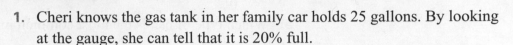

Write About It

1. Cheri knows the gas tank in her family car holds 25 gallons. By looking at the gauge, she can tell that it is 20% full.

   a) How could Cheri find how many gallons of gas 10% of the tank will hold?

   b) How could Cheri use the answer in Part a to find how many gallons of gas are left in the tank?

2. When Gino's cell phone has a full charge, he can talk on it for 3 hours. Use this information to complete the following chart.

Charge as a Percent	Charge as a Fraction	Minutes of Talk Left
a) 100%	1	
b) 30%		
c)		18
d)	$\frac{3}{4}$	
e) $12\frac{1}{2}$%		

3. Copy and shade each container to show it filled to the amount. Show your divisions.

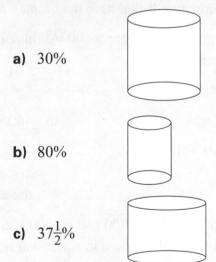

   a) 30%

   b) 80%

   c) $37\frac{1}{2}$%

   d) The full container in Part a holds 10 cups. The container in Part b holds 3 cups. The container in Part c holds 8 cups. Which has the most water in it? Explain your reasoning.

4. Mr. Kokomo has a small pond for goldfish in his backyard. When it is full, it holds 250 gallons of water. It is only 80% full. How much more water will it take to fill it?

5. Mr. Kokomo's pond has 50 fish in it. Twenty percent are koi, $\frac{2}{5}$ are comets, $\frac{3}{10}$ are bubble-eyed goldfish, and the rest are shubunkin goldfish.

a) Which type of fish is the most common in the pond?

b) How many more comets are there then shubunkins?

c) If Mr. Kokomo adds 50 common goldfish to the pond, what percent of the fish in the pond will there be of each type then?

 **Hint**
See page 150

 Think Beyond

d) What if Mr. Kokomo adds 20 common goldfish to the pond instead of 50? What percent of the fish in the pond will there be of each type then?

Think Beyond

6. a) Choose four different digits to make this a true statement:

$\boxed{}$ % of $\boxed{}$ = 12.

b) Can you find more than one way to do this?

Think Back

7. Find the next four numbers in the pattern. Explain the pattern. 122, 118, 114, 110, …

8. A dollar bill is about 6 inches by $2\frac{1}{2}$ inches. What is the perimeter?

9. Name three words that have the prefix *tri-*. What does *tri-* mean?

10. Apples are on sale, 5 for $2.00. At this price, what do a dozen apples cost?

11. Compute:

a) $160 \cdot 25$

b) $1{,}890 \div 18$

c) $460 \cdot 99$

d) Choose one of the problems above and explain how you could find the answer mentally.

12. A plot of land that is 200 feet by 200 feet is about 1 acre. About how many acres are there in a plot that is 400 feet by 400 feet?

A. 1 acre

B. 2 acres

C. 4 acres

D. 16 acres

 Optional Technology Lesson for this section available in your eBook

Sum It Up

In this section, you explored percents, fractions and decimals and connections of the base-10 system to money and to the metric system. The following is a summary of some of the things you should have learned in this section.

Percent-Fraction-Decimal Relationships

- *Percent* means per hundred. For example, 45% means 45 out of 100. This can be written as the decimal 0.45 or the fraction $\frac{45}{100}$.

- There are an infinite number of fractions equivalent to any rational number. For example, $\frac{3}{4} = \frac{6}{8} = \frac{9}{12} = \frac{12}{16}$. You can find equivalent fractions by multiplying or dividing both the numerator and denominator by the same number.

  $\frac{3 \cdot 2}{4 \cdot 2} = \frac{6}{8}$

  $\frac{18 \div 6}{24 \div 6} = \frac{3}{4}$

- There are an infinite number of decimals equivalent to any given number. You can find these by annexing zeros to the right of any decimal number. For example, $0.4 = 0.40 = 0.400 = 0.4000$, and so on.

- Common multiples can be used to find common denominators. The least common multiple can be used to find fractions with the least common denominator. For example, the least common multiple of 8 and 12 is 24. The least common denominator of $\frac{3}{8}$ and $\frac{5}{12}$ is twenty-fourths.

  $\frac{3}{8} = \frac{3 \cdot 3}{8 \cdot 3} = \frac{9}{24}$ and $\frac{5}{12} = \frac{5 \cdot 2}{12 \cdot 2} = \frac{10}{24}$

- Common divisors can be used to simplify fractions. The greatest common divisor can be used to simplify a fraction in one step. For example, the greatest common divisor of 18 and 24 is 6.

  $\frac{18}{24} = \frac{18 \div 6}{24 \div 6} = \frac{3}{4}$

- When using fractions, decimals and percents, it is important to know what one whole is. For example, you might have a gas tank that is 100% full that holds 10 gallons and another that is 50% full that holds 20 gallons. Both tanks would have the same amount of gas.

- An improper fraction can be written as a mixed number by determining the number of wholes and the remaining fraction. For example, $\frac{23}{8}$ is equal to 2 wholes $\left(\frac{16}{8} \text{ or } \frac{8}{8} + \frac{8}{8}\right)$ and $\frac{7}{8}$ so $\frac{23}{8} = 2\frac{7}{8}$.

- You should know decimals and percents that are equal to halves, thirds, fourths, fifths, and tenths.

- Pie charts and circle graphs are used to show how one whole (100%) is split among its parts.

Money and the Metric System

- U.S. money and measurements in the metric system use base-10 systems. That means ten of a smaller unit make up one of the next larger unit. Ten pennies have the same value as one dime; ten centimeters are the same length as one decimeter, and so on. Common metric prefixes are *kilo, hecto, deka, deci, centi,* and *milli*. They relate to place value for numbers larger and smaller than one.

Place Value of Digits Larger Than a Unit			Unit	•	Place Value of Digits Smaller Than a Unit		
thousands	hundreds	tens	ones	•	tenths	hundredths	thousandths
kilo (k)	hecto (h)	deka (da)	meter (m) liter (l) gram (g)	•	deci (d)	centi (c)	milli (m)
Metric Prefixes for Amounts Larger Than a Unit			**Metric Unit**		**Metric Prefixes for Amounts Smaller Than a Unit**		

- Metric rulers are often marked in centimeters and millimeters. Rulers with customary measures often have measures in inches, half inches, quarter inches, eighth inches, and sometimes sixteenth inches.

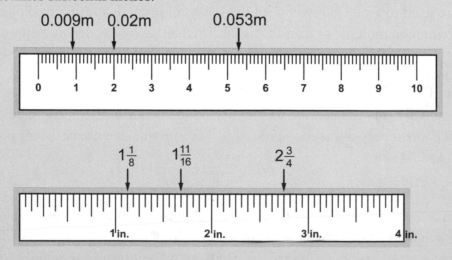

MATHEMATICALLY SPEAKING

Do you know what these mathematical terms mean?

- algorithm
- annex zero
- circle graph
- common denominator
- common fraction
- decimal
- decimal place
- denominator
- divisor
- equivalent decimals
- equivalent fractions
- factor (of a number)
- fraction

- gram
- greatest common divisor (GCD)
- greatest common factor (GCF)
- improper fraction
- integers
- least common denominator (LCD)
- least common multiple (LCM)
- liter
- meter
- mixed number (or numeral)

- multiple
- numerator
- percent
- percent circle
- percent strip
- pie chart
- proper fraction
- rational number
- simplest form (of a fraction)
- simplify (a fraction)
- unit fraction
- whole number

Study Guide

One Number, Many Names

Part 1. What did you learn?

1. Use the words listed under Mathematically Speaking at the end of the Section 1 Sum It Up to fill in the blanks

   One way to compare the _____ $\frac{2}{3}$ and $\frac{3}{4}$ is by finding a
   common _____. You can find a common _____
   for thirds and fourths by finding _____ for 3 and 4. The
   _____ for thirds and fourths is twelfths. 12 is also the
   _____ for 3 and 4 because it is the smallest multiple they
   share. The fractions $\frac{2}{3}$ and $\frac{8}{12}$ are _____ and the fractions
   $\frac{9}{12}$ and $\frac{3}{4}$ are _____. Since $\frac{8}{12}$ is less than $\frac{9}{12}$, we can
   conclude that $\frac{2}{3}$ is _____ $\frac{9}{12}$.

2. Convert each rational number in the chart below to its other two forms. Write all fractions in simplest form. Write improper fractions as mixed numbers.

	Percent	Decimal	Fraction
a.		0.125	
b.			$\frac{3}{4}$
c.	5%		
d.		1.8	
e.			$2\frac{7}{8}$
f.	65%		
g.		0.01	

3. In a recent survey, middle school students were asked whether they prefer listening to music on the radio, on a CD player or on their iPods. The results are shown below.

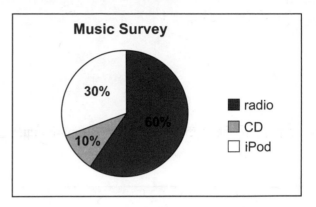

a. What fraction of students prefers listening to music on the radio? Express your answer in two different ways.

b. What fraction of students prefers listening to music on a CD? Express your answer in two different ways.

c. What fraction of students prefers listening to music on their iPods? Express your answer in two different ways.

4. Complete the missing entries in the chart below.

		Amount Shaded Written as a Percent	Amount Shaded Written as a Fraction in Simplest Form	Amount Shaded Written as a Decimal
a.	The entire circle represents 1 whole.			
b.	Each large square represents 1 whole.			

5. Determine which letter is closest to each of the following lengths on the ruler pictured below. Note: The ruler is not drawn to scale.

    a. 0.05 m

    b. 0.25 m

    c. 0.549 m

    d. 78% m

6. Use your inch ruler to draw a line segment of each of the following lengths:

    a. $1\frac{9}{16}$ inches

    b. 2.75% inches

    c. $\frac{31}{8}$ inches

7. Oil is the fuel source for the heat in Miguel's house. The oil is kept in a large tank in Miguel's basement. The tank is currently 20% full with exactly 60 gallons.

    a. What is the capacity of the oil tank when it is full?

    b. How many gallons are in the tank if it is 15% full?

    c. How many gallons are in the tank if it is 0.65 full?

    d. What fraction of the tank is full if it has only 2 gallons of oil?

8. Explain how you could use a string that is $\frac{2}{3}$ of a yard to measure a distance of 1.5 yards.

9. Thea's newborn baby brother, Teddy, is 60 cm in length. Fill in the blanks below:

a. Teddy is _____ dm in length.

b. Teddy is _____ m in length.

c. Teddy is _____ % of a meter in length.

d. Teddy is _____ mm in length.

Part 2. What went wrong?

10. Nathan was asked the following multiple-choice question on a recent quiz.

> In Natalia's garden, 4% of the flowers are geraniums.
> What is 4% written as a decimal?
>
> A. 0.4   C. 0.04
>
> B. 400   D. 4

Nathan chose letter A, but his answer was marked wrong. Why? What could you say or do to help Nathan make sense of the correct answer?

11. Beth-Anne explained to her friend how to write the fraction $\frac{12}{15}$ in simplest form. Here is what she wrote.

$$\frac{12 \div 4}{15 \div 3} = \frac{3}{5}$$

What is wrong with Beth-Anne's work? What could you do or say to help Beth-Anne correctly write $\frac{12}{15}$ in simplest form?

Let's Put Things in Order: Ordering Fractions, Decimals and Percents

Mathematicians often work on a problem using one method and check it using another. This can be fun when you get the same answer and an interesting puzzle when you don't. Moving from fractions to decimals or percents is a good way to better understand rational numbers. In this section, you will continue to think like a mathematician as you explore the relationships among different types of rational numbers by comparing and ordering fractions, decimals and percents.

LESSON 2.1

And the Winner Is ...

 Start It Off

Put these fractions in order from the smallest to the largest:

$$\frac{3}{8}, \frac{5}{8}, \frac{1}{8}, \frac{7}{8}, \frac{9}{8}, \frac{2}{8}$$

Explain your reasoning.

The Big Race

In many sports, rational numbers are used to measure time and distance. In swim meets, some races are so close that times are often reported in hundredths of a second.

1. To the right are the competitors' times for a 100-meter butterfly race:

    a) Put the initial of each swimmer on an arrow on a number line like the one below to show his time.

    b) Who won the race? Who came in last?

    c) How many seconds apart did Bart and Ed finish?

    d) Gina said that the slowest swimmer was less than 2 seconds behind the fastest swimmer. Was she correct?

NOTE If you think about place value when you read decimals, it will be easy to write them in fraction form. For example, 0.4 should not be read as "point four." It is "four-tenths," which can also be written as $\frac{4}{10}$. Thirty-eight hundredths can be written as either 0.38 or $\frac{38}{100}$.

---

2. Ed said that $\frac{4}{10} = \frac{40}{100} = \frac{400}{1,000} = \frac{4,000}{10,000}$.

    a) Explain why this pattern works using what you know about equivalent fractions.

    b) Write each of the fractions as a decimal. Think about place value. What rule does this pattern suggest about equivalent decimals?

3. Franco thinks that $0.9 = 0.09 = 0.009$.

    a) Write Franco's decimals as fractions.

    b) Are the fractions equivalent? Is Franco correct?

4. In another meet, the women swam the 200-meter freestyle. One of the scorekeepers decided to record some of their times as fractional parts of a minute, some as minutes and seconds, and some as decimals. The women said that the times were hard to compare.

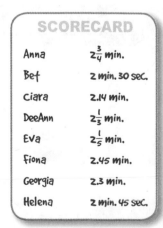

a) How can you rewrite the list of times using equivalent numbers that are easier to compare? Rewrite these times and compare your work to a partner's. Did you rewrite them the same way? Is the order from fastest to slowest the same?

b) Put the initial of each swimmer on an arrow on the number line below to show her time.

c) Georgia said her time was the same as Bet's. Was she correct? Explain. Were there any other ties?

d) Georgia also said that she must have beat Ciara because they both took a little more than 2 minutes, and 3 is less than 14. Was she correct? Explain.

e) How many seconds apart were Anna and Bet? Write the difference as a fraction and as a percent of a minute.

f) Make up questions about the race and challenge a partner to answer them. Do you both agree on the answers?

GAME · · · · · Racing Times Challenge · · · · ·

Players: 5 – 6 in each group

Materials: Racing Times cards (1 per player)

As a group, put your cards in order from fastest time to slowest time. Next, join another group and combine your cards. Put the combined cards in order from fastest time to slowest time. If you do not all agree, use a number line like the one below to help you decide.

 **Think Beyond** Create your own game using the **Racing Times** cards or a set of your own cards that use decimals, fractions and percents. Your game should make the players think about the order of the numbers on your cards.

Garth made up a set of **Racing Times** cards with lots of decimals. He said ordering decimals is like putting words in alphabetical order. For words, you first look at the first letter and put those in order. When the first letter is the same, you look at the second letter, and so forth. With numbers, you first look at the whole numbers and put those in order. You then look at the tenths.

5. Finish Garth's directions for ordering decimals. Use these times from Garth's Racing Times cards as examples: 14.43, 13.2, 13.15, 13.23, 14.5, 14.4, 13.156, 14.500.

6. Tonya said that when she put Garth's cards in order, she first changed them all to equivalent decimals in thousandths. She said that she could just look at the whole numbers and then the three digits to the right of the decimal point that make up the thousandths to decide the order. Explain how Tonya might do that. Was she correct?

7. Virginia said that the following are ordered from least to greatest.

   2.1   2.004   2.07   2.25   2.031

   a) What went wrong? Why do you think Virginia put the numbers in this order?

   b) What is the correct order? How would you help Virginia understand this?

Wrap It Up

Rational numbers can be difficult to compare if some are written as fractions and some are written as decimals. Explain two different ways you might order rational numbers from least to greatest. Use the following numbers in your explanation: $2\frac{3}{4}$, 2.8, 2.62, $2\frac{4}{5}$, 2.625, $2\frac{5}{8}$.

LESSON
2.1

SECTION 2

On Your Own

MATERIALS LIST

▶ Lesson Guide 2.1:
  On Your Own

Write About It

1. Put the following in order from least to greatest and explain your method.

   a) 1.234, 12.34, 1.3, 1.23, 1.300, 1.03, 1.030, 1.003

   b) $2\frac{2}{3}$ min., 2 min. 45 sec., 2.6 min., $2\frac{3}{4}$ min., 2.25 min.

2. To qualify for the Olympic Team Trials for the 50-meter freestyle, a female swimmer must swim the race in less than 26.39 seconds.

   a) Samara swam the distance in 26.4 seconds. Did she qualify?

   b) Janine swam the distance in 26.281 seconds. Did she qualify? Explain.

3. On a recent national test, only 10% of 13-year-old students and 8% of 17-year-old students could list a reasonable value for point A. Explain what they should have answered.

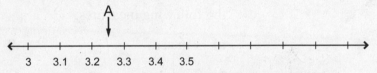

4. In 1935, Jesse Owens set a long-jump record that held for 25 years. He jumped 8.13 meters. In 1989, Dion Bentley, a high school student, had a long jump of 8.09 meters. Was his jump longer than Jesse Owens'? Explain.

5. In the same track meet in 1935, Jesse's time of 22.6 seconds in the 220-yard low hurdles beat the old world record by 0.4 second. What was the old record?

6. Before Jesse ran the 200-yard dash, the world record was 20.6 seconds. Jesse beat the record by 0.30 second. What was his time?

7. At a recent high school track meet, girls in the 200-meter dash had:

   a) List the girls in order from first to last place. Write their times in decimals and as fractions with a common denominator.

   SCORECARD

Jasmine	$25\frac{3}{10}$ sec.
Devan	24.54 sec.
Vanessa	25.8 sec.
Aubrey	$24\frac{3}{5}$ sec.
Shanae	$24\frac{1}{4}$ sec.
Caitlin	25.78 sec.
Montrece	25.09 sec.

b) Put an arrow and the initial of each girl next to her time on a number line like the one below.

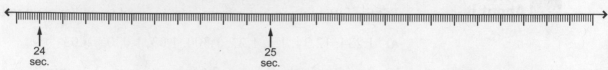

24 sec.   25 sec.

c) Vanessa said that her 25.8 seconds is faster than Caitlin's 25.78 seconds because 8 is less than 78. Caitlin said that 25.78 seconds is actually a tiny bit faster. Who was right? Explain.

8. On a recent national test, less than half of the 13-year-old students could name the greatest number in this list: 0.19, 0.036, 0.195, 0.2. Write an explanation that would help them determine the greatest number.

Think Back

9. Name things in your home or classroom that have approximately the following measures:

a) 3 meters

d) $\frac{1}{2}$ yard

b) 0.2 meter

e) 1 quart

c) 6 inches

10. Put $+, -, \cdot$ or $\div$ in each circle to make the following true. Don't forget the correct order of operations.

a) 18 ◯ 9 = 2

d) 4 ◯ 2 ◯ 3 = 11

b) 45 ◯ 40 ◯ 5 = 10

e) 4 ◯ 2 ◯ 3 = 24

c) 4 ◯ 2 ◯ 3 = 10

11. Which of the following is incorrect?

A. $25 \cdot 100 = 2{,}500$

C. $98{,}000 \div 1{,}000 = 98$

B. $3{,}600 \div 10 = 36$

D. $1{,}000 \cdot 78 = 78{,}000$

12. A rectangle is 4 feet by 3 feet. If you double both the length and the width, what is the area of the new rectangle? How does this compare to the area of the original rectangle?

13. There are 12 books in a box and 15 boxes in a container. How many books are in 100 containers?

Is This Right?

 Start It Off

Put these fractions in order from the smallest to the largest:

$\frac{3}{4}, \frac{3}{2}, \frac{3}{8}, \frac{3}{5}$

Explain your reasoning.

The Great Decimal Debate

Mr. Jacobs's sixth grade class was discussing the size of numbers. Steve said that for whole numbers, the number with the most digits is always the largest and the number with the fewest digits is always the smallest. He thought that should work for decimals as well.

1. Is Steve's rule always right for whole numbers? Is it always wrong? Is it sometimes right and sometimes wrong? Give several examples.

2. Is Steve's rule always right for decimals? Is it always wrong? Is it sometimes right and sometimes wrong? Give several examples. Use a number line to assist in your explanation.

Lori said that when you put a zero in a whole number, it always changes the value of the number, but when you put a zero in a decimal number, the value of the number does not change.

3. Is Lori's statement about whole numbers always right? Is it always wrong? Is it sometimes right and sometimes wrong? Give several examples.

4. Is Lori's statement about decimals always right? Is it always wrong? Is it sometimes right and sometimes wrong? Give several examples. Use a number line to assist in your explanation.

5. When deciding which of two decimals is larger, what other rules or patterns do you look for? Explain your ideas to a partner.

The Great Fraction Debate

Students (and adults) often try to use whole number rules with fractions and find that they only work sometimes. Thinking about why rules work, rather than simply trying to memorize them, can help you to better understand them.

6. One way to compare fractions is to rewrite them with a common denominator and then compare the numerators. For example, consider three fractions from Start It Off: $\frac{3}{4}$, $\frac{3}{2}$ and $\frac{3}{8}$. How might you compare these fractions using common denominators? Discuss your thinking with a partner.

7. Paul said that you can never have zero in the numerator of a fraction. Shelby said that you could have zero in the numerator but not in the denominator. Tim said that you could never have zero in either the numerator or the denominator. Discuss with a partner who was right. Be prepared to share your reasoning with the class.

More Fraction Comparisons

Finding a common denominator is only one way to compare fractions. Another way is finding a common numerator. Note that $\frac{3}{4}$, $\frac{3}{2}$ and $\frac{3}{8}$ have a common numerator.

8. How might you use the idea of common numerators and the size of the denominator to order $\frac{3}{4}$, $\frac{3}{2}$ and $\frac{3}{8}$ from greatest to least?

9. Use the idea of common numerators to order $\frac{4}{5}$, $\frac{4}{9}$ and $\frac{2}{3}$.

   a) Talk to a partner about whether $\frac{4}{5}$ or $\frac{4}{9}$ is greater.

   b) How might you rename $\frac{2}{3}$ as an equivalent fraction with the same numerator as $\frac{4}{5}$ and $\frac{4}{9}$? How does $\frac{2}{3}$ compare to $\frac{4}{5}$ and $\frac{4}{9}$?

MATHEMATICALLY SPEAKING

▶ benchmark

You might also use benchmarks when ordering fractions. A benchmark is a value—such as 0, $\frac{1}{2}$, or 1—that is easy to compare with other numbers. For example, if you want to compare $\frac{3}{8}$ and $\frac{5}{9}$, you might first decide whether each number is greater than or less than $\frac{1}{2}$. Since 3 is less than half of 8 and 5 is more than half of 9, you know that $\frac{3}{8}$ is less than $\frac{1}{2}$ and $\frac{5}{9}$ is greater than $\frac{1}{2}$.

10. How do $\frac{3}{8}$ and $\frac{5}{9}$ compare? Explain.

11. Use benchmarks to order the following from least to greatest: $\frac{1}{2}, \frac{3}{8}, \frac{5}{9}, \frac{11}{10}, \frac{1}{11}$. Compare your results with a partner.

When both fractions are close to a benchmark, such as 1, you can use the idea of missing parts to determine which is greater. For example, $\frac{11}{12}$ is $\frac{1}{12}$ from 1. $\frac{4}{5}$ is $\frac{1}{5}$ from 1.

12. **a)** Which is greater, $\frac{1}{12}$ or $\frac{1}{5}$?

   b) Which is greater, $\frac{11}{12}$ or $\frac{4}{5}$?

   c) How can you use missing parts to answer Part b?

13. Use missing parts to order the following fractions: $\frac{12}{13}, \frac{6}{7}, \frac{7}{8}, \frac{9}{10}$. Discuss your reasoning with a partner.

⬆Wrap It Up

MATHEMATICALLY SPEAKING

▶ benchmark

Fractions can be compared using a variety of methods. You can write all the fractions as equivalent decimals and compare decimals, but you can also make the comparisons using only fractions. Methods for comparing fractions include using common numerators, common denominators, benchmarks and missing parts. Explain how to use each of these methods. Illustrate each with at least four fractions.

LESSON
2.2

SECTION 2

On Your Own

MATERIALS LIST

▶ Lesson Guide 2.2:
   On Your Own

Write About It

1. On a recent national test, only 2% of 13-year-old students could order the numbers below from least to greatest. Explain how you might do this using at least one of the following techniques: common denominators, common numerators, benchmarks and missing parts.

   $\frac{5}{8}, \frac{3}{10}, \frac{3}{5}, \frac{1}{4}, \frac{2}{3}, \frac{1}{2}$

2. **a)** List three other decimals that are equivalent to 0.3.

   b) How can you show that the decimals are equivalent using a number line?

   c) Write 0.3 as a fraction. Write two other fractions equivalent to three-tenths with denominators that are powers of ten (that is, 10, 100, 1,000, and so on). Show that the fractions are equivalent. How does this compare to writing equivalent decimals?

3. When a fraction is written in simplest form, some people say that the fraction has been "reduced." Why do you think that we prefer the term "simplifying a fraction" to "reducing a fraction"?

4. Fill in the table below to express each number in four ways: in words, as a mixed number or fraction with a denominator that is a power of ten, as a decimal, and as a mixed number or fraction in simplest form.

Rational Number in Words	Mixed Number or Fraction— Denominator Power of 10	Decimal	Mixed Number or Fraction— Simplest Form
twenty-four hundredths			
		13.50	
	$6\frac{900}{1,000}$		
twenty-four and six-hundredths			
		2.025	

5. $\frac{1}{15} < \frac{1}{16}$ True or false? Explain.

6. Order each from least to greatest and name the strategy that you use.

a) $\dfrac{3}{8}, \dfrac{3}{10}, \dfrac{3}{7}, \dfrac{3}{5}$

b) $\dfrac{3}{5}, \dfrac{1}{5}, \dfrac{2}{5}, \dfrac{7}{5}$

c) $\dfrac{8}{9}, \dfrac{11}{12}, \dfrac{12}{13}, \dfrac{6}{7}$

d) $\dfrac{11}{10}, \dfrac{3}{7}, \dfrac{9}{11}, \dfrac{5}{8}$

7. Reg and Kelly were arguing about where to place $1\dfrac{1}{2}$ on this number line. They decided on the following points.

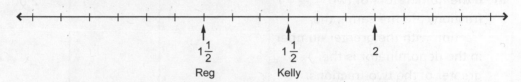

a) If Reg is correct, where is 1 located? Where is 0? Copy and label the number line to show this.

b) If Kelly is correct, where is 1? Where is 0? Make another copy of the number line and label it to show this.

8. Examine the fractions $\dfrac{2}{3}, \dfrac{4}{6}, \dfrac{6}{9}, \dfrac{8}{12}$ and $\dfrac{10}{15}$.

a) List three patterns that you notice.

b) How is each fraction related to the others?

c) Write a recursive rule for finding the next fraction in the list.

d) Predict the twentieth term.

e) Write an explicit rule for the nth term.

Think Beyond

9. For each of the following arguments, decide if the statement is always, sometimes or never true, assuming you never have a zero in the denominator. Use words, examples and/or drawings to explain your answers.

Statement	Always, Sometimes or Never True	Explanation	Examples	Drawings
a) If the numerators of two fractions are the same, the fraction with the greater number in the denominator is the greater of the two fractions.			$3 > 2$ but $\frac{1}{3} < \frac{1}{2}$	
b) If the denominators of two fractions are the same, the fraction with the greater number in the numerator is the greater of the two fractions.				
c) If you multiply the numerator and denominator of a fraction by the same number, the new fraction is equivalent to the original.				
d) If you divide the numerator and denominator of a fraction by the same number, the new fraction is equivalent to the original fraction.				

e) All the examples on the chart assume that you never have a zero in the denominator of a fraction. Why can't you have a zero in the denominator? Can you have a zero in the numerator? Explain.

10. How might you compare $\frac{5}{7}$ and $\frac{7}{9}$ using missing parts and common numerators?

Think Beyond

11. I am thinking of a number from this list: $\frac{4}{6}, \frac{5}{9}, \frac{5}{12}, \frac{9}{15}, \frac{11}{15}$

- It is greater than one-half.
- It is less than two-thirds.
- It is in simplest form.

What number am I thinking of?

Make up your own riddle for another number on the list.

Think Beyond

12. When ordering fractions, if $\frac{a}{b} < \frac{c}{d}$ and $\frac{c}{d} < \frac{e}{f}$ is it always true that $\frac{a}{b} < \frac{e}{f}$? Use the Internet to look up the transitive property of inequality and explain how it relates to your answer.

Think Back

13. Between 1946 and 1991, there were 288,324,898 automobiles scrapped in the United States.

   a) Write this amount in words.

   b) Is this more or less than $\frac{1}{4}$ of a billion cars?

14. Find the area of the shaded region.

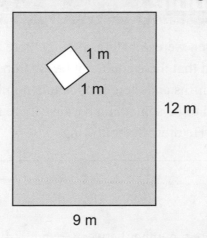

15. Which number is 1 more than a multiple of 5?

   A. 136

   B. 45

   C. 264

   D. 900

16. Paul is 2 years older than Peter. In 12 years, Peter will be 29. How old is Paul today?

17. Cory has test scores of 84, 91, 100 and 85.

   a) What is his average?

   b) If Cory gets 100 on his next test, how much will his average increase?

18. If you spin the following spinner 200 times, about how many times would you expect it to land on 3?

What Comes Between?

➡️ Start It Off

Put these fractions in order from the smallest to the largest:

$\frac{6}{7}, \frac{2}{3}, \frac{5}{6}, \frac{3}{4}$

Explain your reasoning.

Fractions in the Middle

Bernie and Ben were debating whether there is a number between $\frac{2}{5}$ and $\frac{3}{5}$. Bernie said that there could not be anything between them because both numbers are fifths and there is no whole number between 2 and 3. Ben said that there had to be something because there is space between them on the number line. He drew the following:

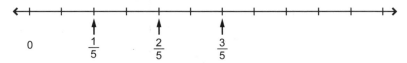

1. **a)** Is there a number between $\frac{2}{5}$ and $\frac{3}{5}$? Explain.

    b) What number is halfway between $\frac{2}{5}$ and $\frac{3}{5}$? How did you figure it out?

Hint
See page 150

    c) Are there other points between $\frac{2}{5}$ and $\frac{3}{5}$? If so, list two other points. If not, explain why not.

Measurements in the Middle

Victoria is measuring the length of her pencil. She says it is a bit longer than 0.1 meter, or 1 decimeter. Jack says that Victoria should be more accurate. Victoria says the pencil is shorter than a tenth of a meter, plus half of a tenth of a meter.

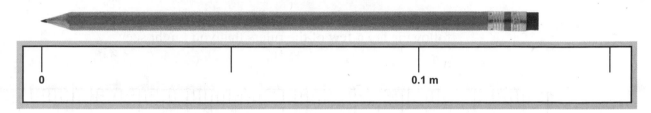

2. Talk to a partner about whether Victoria is correct. How might she be more accurate?

3. Look at a meterstick.

    a) What is another name for a hundredth of a meter?

    b) How might you use a meterstick to find a more accurate measurement than 0.1 meter?

    c) Look at the ruler below. What is the measure of the pencil to the nearest hundredth of a meter?

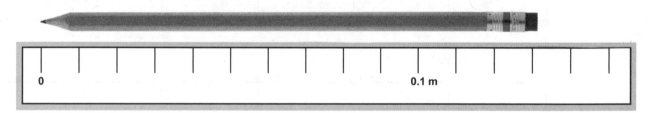

4. Meg has a ruler that has smaller markings than hundredths of a meter. There are 10 of these in each centimeter.

    a) Meg knows that the small markings are millimeters. What part of a meter is each millimeter? Write your answer as a fraction and as a decimal.

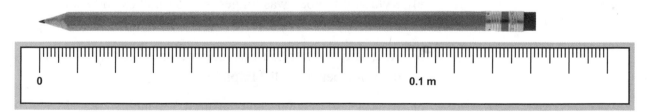

    b) What is the length of the pencil to the nearest millimeter? What is this as a part of a meter? Write your answer as a decimal and a fraction.

c) Do you think there are units that are smaller than a millimeter? Why might those be useful?

d) If you want to make the most accurate measurement possible, would you prefer to use a ruler that has markings for decimeters, centimeters or millimeters? Why?

e) Mathematicians say that measurements can never be exact. Why?

Inch rulers sometimes show different fractional parts of an inch. The following are a few of the rulers that you might see.

I)

II)

III)

IV)

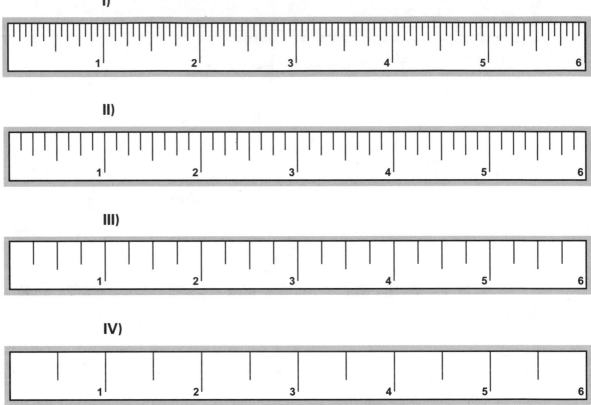

5. Which of the rulers would you choose to make the most accurate measurement? Explain.

6. Kyle, Kate and Keisha each measured a pen.

a) Kyle said the pen was longer than $5\frac{1}{2}$ inches and shorter than 6 inches. List two possible lengths for the pen.

b) Kate said that her pen was longer than $5\frac{3}{4}$ inches. Could Kate have the same pen as Kyle? Explain.

c) Keisha said that her pen measured $5\frac{9}{16}$ inches. If Kyle, Kate and Keisha all measured accurately, could they all have the same pen? Explain.

After discussing measurements, play the **Guess My Number** game.

 · · · · · **Guess My Number** · · · · ·

Players: Two (or two teams)

Goal: To guess a secret number

DIRECTIONS:

Player 1 writes down a secret number. The number must be less than 10 and may have up to two decimal places.

Player 2 then tries to guess the number.

Player 1 tells whether the guess is too big, too little or just right.

Player 2 continues to guess until the number is named.

START OF A SAMPLE GAME:

Ann writes down 3.24.

Bill guesses 5 and Ann tells him the guess is too big.

Bill guesses 2.5 and Ann tells him the guess is too small.

Bill guesses 3 and Ann tells him it is still too small.

Bill tries 3.5 and Ann says "too big."

Bill tries 3.3. Ann says "still too big."

Bill says 3.2.

 Think Beyond Play the game with fractions instead of decimals. Use only numbers that can be found on an inch ruler marked in sixteenths.

7. Use the game that Ann and Bill are playing to answer the following:

   a) What should Ann reply when Bill says 3.2?

   b) Would 3.14 be a good next guess for Bill? Why?

   c) If Bill guesses 3.22, how far is he from Ann's number?

 **rap It Up**

The heights of two plants are described below:

Plant A: More than $2\frac{3}{8}$ inches and less than $2\frac{1}{2}$ inches

Plant B: More than 0.21 meter and less than 0.22 meter.

   a) Explain how you might find one possible height for plant A.

   b) Many people would say that there is no number between 0.21 and 0.22, so a plant could not have a measure between these two amounts. How would you respond?

 Write About It

1. Jason said he could find a number between any two numbers.

   a) Meredith challenged him to find a number between 0.45 meter and 0.46 meter. Explain how Jason might do this.

   b) Name two measurements between $\frac{7}{8}$ inch and 1 inch.

   c) Why do mathematicians say that measurements can never be exact?

2. George was measuring his calculator. He first used a ruler that had markings only for inches and half inches.

   a) What is the width of George's calculator to the nearest half-inch? What two measurements does this fall between?

   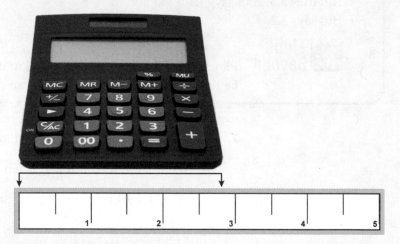

   b) What is the width of George's calculator to the nearest eighth-inch? What two measurements does this fall between?

c) What is the width of George's calculator to the nearest sixteenth-inch? What two measurements does this fall between?

d) Name two decimals between $\frac{3}{4}$ and $\frac{7}{8}$.

3. Dirk needs $2\frac{3}{8}$ cups of flour for his cookie recipe. He has only a 1-cup measuring cup that is marked in fourths. How might he accurately measure $2\frac{3}{8}$ cups?

4. Are there any numbers between 0.125 and $\frac{1}{8}$? Explain.

5. Name one fraction and one decimal between 0.62 and 0.63.

6. Many electronic devices use measurements that are much more accurate than millimeters or sixteenths of an inch. Do you think that they use the metric or our customary (English) system of measurement? Explain.

 Think Beyond

7. A helium atom has a measurement of 31 picometers. A picometer is one-millionth of a millionth of a meter.

a) Write 1 picometer as a decimal.

b) Write a number that is more than 30 picometers and less than 31 picometers.

Think Back

8. If you add 15 to a number and then multiply the sum by 6, your final product is 126. What is the original number?

9. 4! is read "4 factorial" and means $4 \cdot 3 \cdot 2 \cdot 1$. In general, factorial means to multiply the given whole number by each counting number less than it.

a) $4! = $ _____

b) What number will be in the ones place for 5!?

 **Think Beyond**

c) What number will be in the ones place for 12!? Explain.

10. Look at the bus schedule to answer the following.

    a) If Karen gets on the bus at Chapel St. and Fleming Ave. in Newark at 6:51 am, at what time should she get to 16th Ave. at 18th St.?

    b) Mark works at Springfield Ave. and Martin Luther King Jr. Blvd. in Newark and must be at work before 8:30 am. He gets on the bus at the River Terminal in Kearny. What time should he catch the bus? Explain.

JERSEY CITY - Exchange Place Terminal (Montgomery St. at Greene St.)	JERSEY CITY Communipaw Ave. at Grand St.	JERSEY CITY Journal Square Trans. Center	JERSEY CITY Communipaw Ave. at West Side Ave.	KEARNY River Terminal (Central Ave.)	NEWARK Euclid Ave. at Lockwood St.	NEWARK Chapel St. at Fleming Ave.	NEWARK - Penn Station Market St. Bus Lane at Raymond Plaza W.	NEWARK Market St. at Broad St.	NEWARK - Springfield Ave. at Martin Luther King Jr. Blvd.	NEWARK 16th Ave. at 18th St.	NEWARK 18th Ave. at West End Ave.	NEWARK Ivy Hill Loop (Mt. Vernon Pl.)
A.M.	A.M.	A.M.	A.M.	A.M.	A.M.	A.M.	A.M.	A.M.	A.M.	A.M.	A.M.	A.M.
5.10	5.20	–	5.26	5.35	–	5.41	5.47	5.50	5.54	6.05	6.13	6.17
–	–	–	–	–	5.48	5.50	5.56	5.59	6.03	6.14	6.22	6.26
–	–	–	–	5.50	–	5.56	6.02	6.05	6.09	6.20	6.28	6.32
5.40	5.50	–	5.56	–	–	6.05	6.11	6.14	6.18	6.29	6.37	6.41
–	–	–	–	6.07	–	6.13	6.19	6.22	6.26	6.37	6.45	6.49
–	–	5.55	6.05	6.14	–	6.20	6.26	6.29	6.33	6.44	6.52	6.56
–	–	–	–	–	6.28	6.30	6.36	6.39	6.43	6.54	7.02	7.06
–	–	–	–	–	6.38	6.40	6.46	6.49	6.53	7.04	7.12	7.16
–	–	–	–	–	6.49	6.51	6.57	7.00	7.04	7.18	7.26	7.30
6.26	6.36	–	6.42	6.51	–	6.57	7.03	7.07	7.11	7.25	–	–
–	–	–	–	6.54	–	7.00	7.10	7.14	7.18	7.32	7.40	7.44
–	–	–	–	–	7.01	7.03	7.13	7.17	7.21	7.35	7.43	7.47
–	–	6.44	6.54	7.03	–	7.09	7.19	7.23	7.27	7.41	–	–
–	–	–	–	7.11	–	7.13	7.23	7.27	7.31	7.45	7.53	7.57
–	–	–	–	7.10	–	7.16	7.26	7.30	7.34	7.48	7.56	8.00
6.51	7.01	–	7.09	–	–	7.19	7.29	7.33	7.37	7.51	–	–
–	–	7.04	7.16	–	–	7.26	7.36	7.40	7.44	7.58	8.06	8.10
–	–	–	–	–	7.35	7.37	7.47	7.51	7.55	8.09	8.17	8.21
–	–	–	–	7.37	–	7.43	7.53	7.57	8.01	8.15	–	–
–	–	–	–	7.43	–	7.49	7.59	8.03	8.07	8.21	8.29	8.33
–	–	–	–	–	7.51	7.53	8.03	8.07	8.11	8.25	8.33	8.37
7.25	7.35	–	7.43	7.52	–	7.58	8.08	8.12	8.16	8.30	–	–
–	–	–	–	7.56	–	8.02	8.12	8.16	8.20	8.34	8.42	8.46
–	–	7.44	7.56	–	–	8.06	8.16	8.20	8.24	8.38	–	–
–	–	–	–	8.05	–	8.11	8.21	8.25	8.29	8.43	8.51	8.55
–	–	–	–	–	8.14	8.16	8.26	8.30	8.34	8.48	8.56	9.00
7.48	7.58	–	8.06	8.15	–	8.21	8.31	8.35	8.39	8.53	9.01	9.05
–	–	–	–	–	8.24	8.26	8.36	8.40	8.44	8.58	–	–
–	–	8.09	8.21	–	–	8.31	8.41	8.45	8.49	9.03	9.11	9.15
–	–	–	–	–	8.34	8.36	8.46	8.50	8.54	9.08	9.16	9.20
8.13	8.23	–	8.31	–	–	8.41	8.51	8.55	8.59	9.13	–	–
–	–	8.24	8.36	8.45	–	8.46	8.56	9.00	9.04	9.18	9.26	9.30
–	–	–	–	–	8.44	8.51	9.01	9.04	9.08	9.22	9.30	9.34
–	–	–	8.53	–	8.55	8.57	9.07	9.10	9.14	9.28	–	–
8.35	8.45	–	–	–	–	9.03	9.11	9.14	9.18	9.32	9.40	9.44
–	–	–	–	–	9.06	9.08	9.16	9.19	9.23	9.37	–	–
–	–	–	–	–	9.11	9.13	9.21	9.24	9.28	9.42	9.50	9.54
–	–	8.56	9.08	–	–	9.18	9.26	9.29	9.33	9.47	9.55	9.59

11. The temperature has been falling at an average of 3 degrees per hour all day. At 9 pm, the temperature was 45°F. What was the temperature at 6 am that day?

12. A movie costs $8.50 for an adult and $5.25 for a child. If Mr. and Mrs. Tully take their three children to the movies, how much will it cost to get in?

Optional Technology for this section av[ailable] in your eBook

Sum It Up

In this section, you thought like a mathematician as you explored relationships among different types of rational numbers by comparing and ordering factions, decimals and percents.

Ordering Decimals and Fractions

■ When ordering decimals, you can use a method that is similar to determining alphabetical order, first ordering the whole numbers, then the tenths, then the hundredths, and so on. You may also change the decimals to equivalent fractions and order those.

■ When zeros are annexed to the right of a decimal, the value of the decimal does not change. For example, $0.3 = 0.30 = 0.300$. This can also be shown with equivalent fractions as $\frac{3}{10} = \frac{30}{100} = \frac{300}{1,000}$.

■ If zeros are inserted to the right of the decimal point and to the left of any of the nonzero digits in a decimal, the new number will not be equivalent to the original decimal. For example, $0.7 \neq 0.07 \neq 0.007$. This can also be shown with fractions: $\frac{7}{10} \neq \frac{7}{100} \neq \frac{7}{1,000}$.

■ A number line can be used to assist with ordering rational numbers. For example, to put the decimals 0.2, 0.31, 0.23, 0.09 and 0.3 in order, you might first place them on the following number line.

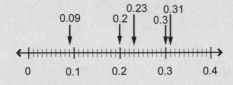

■ A number of different strategies may be used to order fractions. A common method is to divide the numerator by the denominator to change the fractions into decimals and then order the decimals. Several other methods are also useful:

• **Common denominators.** Fractions may be written with common denominators and then the numerators may be compared. For example, to compare $\frac{3}{4}, \frac{1}{2}$ and $\frac{2}{3}$, rewrite the three fractions as equivalent fractions with a denominator of 12. The fractions would then be $\frac{9}{12}, \frac{6}{12}$ and $\frac{8}{12}$. Because these are all twelfths, the fraction with the least number of twelfths is the least number, and the fraction with the greatest number of twelfths is the greatest. Ordered from least to greatest, these would be $\frac{6}{12}, \frac{8}{12}, \frac{9}{12}$ or $\frac{1}{2}, \frac{2}{3}, \frac{3}{4}$.

- **Common numerators.** Fractions that have the same numerators may be compared by the size of their denominators. For example, to compare $\frac{3}{4}$, $\frac{3}{2}$ and $\frac{3}{5}$ you should realize that you have three of each piece. If the unit is the same, halves are larger than fourths and fourths are larger than fifths. The order from least to greatest is $\frac{3}{5}$, $\frac{3}{4}$, $\frac{3}{2}$.

- **Benchmarks.** Fractions may also be compared to benchmarks such as 0, $\frac{1}{2}$ and 1. For example, to order $\frac{5}{8}$, $\frac{13}{12}$ and $\frac{2}{5}$ you might think $\frac{2}{5} < \frac{1}{2}$, $\frac{1}{2} < \frac{5}{8}$ and $1 < \frac{13}{12}$, so the order from least to greatest is $\frac{2}{5}$, $\frac{5}{8}$, $\frac{13}{12}$.

- **Missing parts.** If fractions are all close to the same benchmark, such as 1, you may be able to order them by the amount needed to make 1. For example, if you want to know if $\frac{8}{9}$ is larger or smaller than $\frac{9}{10}$, you might think that $\frac{8}{9}$ is $\frac{1}{9}$ less than 1 and $\frac{9}{10}$ is $\frac{1}{10}$ less than 1. Since $\frac{1}{10} < \frac{1}{9}$, $\frac{9}{10}$ is closer to 1 than $\frac{8}{9}$ is. Therefore, $\frac{8}{9} < \frac{9}{10}$.

■ If some numbers are written as fractions and some as decimals, you can write them all in the same form before ordering them. For example, to order 0.24, $\frac{3}{8}$, 0.3, $\frac{1}{4}$ and 0.32, rewrite them as decimals with the same number of decimal places or as fractions with a common denominator: 0.240, 0.375, 0.300, 0.250, 0.320 or $\frac{240}{1,000}$, $\frac{375}{1,000}$, $\frac{300}{1,000}$, $\frac{250}{1,000}$, $\frac{320}{1,000}$. Once they are rewritten in the same form, they can be easily ordered.

■ To put times that use fractions, decimals, or minutes and seconds in order, rewrite them all in the same form before ordering.

Numbers in Between

■ Unlike the set of whole numbers, there is always a rational number between any two nonequivalent rational numbers.

- To find a decimal between two decimals such as 0.34 and 0.35, you might first write these as equivalent decimals such as 0.340 and 0.350. You can then find several decimals between these such as 0.341, 0.342, 0.343, and so on.

- To find a fraction between two fractions such as $\frac{2}{5}$ and $\frac{3}{5}$, you might write these as equivalent fractions such as $\frac{4}{10}$ and $\frac{6}{10}$ or $\frac{8}{20}$ and $\frac{12}{20}$. You can then find fractions between them such as $\frac{5}{10}$, or $\frac{1}{2}$, and $\frac{9}{20}$.

■ Between any two different measures, there is always another measure. Rulers may be divided into smaller parts to show this. For example, to find a point between 0.01 and 0.02 meter, you may use a metric ruler such as this.

To find a measure between $1\frac{5}{8}$ and $1\frac{6}{8}$ inches, you may use an inch ruler such as this.

MATHEMATICALLY SPEAKING

Do you know what this mathematical term means?

▶ benchmark

Study Guide

Let's Put Things in Order: Ordering Fractions, Decimals and Percents

Part 1. What did you learn?

1. Bryana, Jessie, Emily and Taryn ran one lap around the track outside their school. Their times were $2\frac{1}{3}$ minutes, 2.25 minutes, $\frac{8}{3}$ minutes, and 2 minutes and 30 seconds. Order these times from least to greatest.

2. Determine which letter on the number line is closest to each of the following times: $2\frac{1}{3}$ minutes, 1.25 minutes, $\frac{8}{3}$ minutes, and 1 minute and 30 seconds.

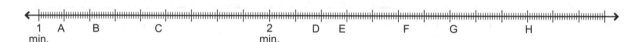

3. Order these lengths from least to greatest: 75% of a meter, 0.4 meter, 40 millimeters, $40\frac{1}{4}$ centimeters.

4. Determine a reasonable value for each of the locations on the ruler.

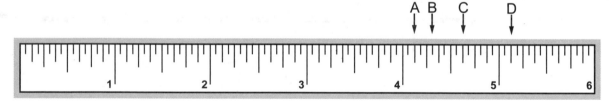

5. List the following numbers in order from least to greatest: 2.4, 2.006, and 2.20.

6. Divi compared two fractions by converting them to the fractions $\frac{12}{32}$ and $\frac{12}{21}$ because they had common numerators. What might the original numbers have been? Which fraction is greater? How do you know?

7. SuAnne knows different methods for comparing fractions (common denominator, common numerator, benchmarks, missing parts), but gets confused about when to use each method. Which method(s) would you recommend SuAnne use for each of the pairs below? Explain your choices.

   a. $\frac{4}{5}$ and $\frac{5}{6}$

   b. $\frac{6}{5}$ and $\frac{13}{10}$

   c. $\frac{3}{5}$ and $\frac{6}{11}$

8. Fill in the blanks with two non-equivalent fractions:

   $\frac{3}{5} <$ _____ $<$ _____ $< \frac{4}{5}$.

9. Fill in the blanks with two non-equivalent decimals:

   $0.36 <$ _____ $<$ _____ < 0.37.

10. Compare the size of the fraction and decimal (using $<$, $>$ or $=$).

   a. $1\frac{4}{5}$ and 1.45

   b. $\frac{4}{5}$ and 0.85

   c. $1\frac{1}{5}$ and 1.25

11. Phil's science class is measuring the growth of a plant over time. Three students reported that their plants grew between 2.3 and 2.4 centimeters in 1 week. Give three possible measurements that are between 2.3 and 2.4 cm.

12. DeAnne measured the length of her room. She found that it was between $\frac{37}{3}$ feet and $\frac{38}{3}$ feet. Give three possible measurements for the length of DeAnne's room. List one as an improper fraction, one as a decimal, and one as a mixed number.

13. Jabar, Kyle and Lisa came up with three reasonable but different estimates for the length of the paper clip pictured below. What might each of their estimates have been?

Part 2. What went wrong?

14. Zara is confused about zeros and decimals. She doesn't understand when it is okay to annex a zero and when it is not. For example, she knows that 2.30 = 2.3 = 2.300 and 0.4 = 0.40, but she also thinks that 2.030 = 2.3. What would you say or do to help Zara understand when she can annex a zero to a decimal and when she can't?

15. Dimitri wrote that 2 minutes and 30 seconds was the same as 2.30 since, "seconds are parts of a minute." What is wrong with Dimitri's reasoning?

16. Carole was asked to convert 2.75 minutes into a fraction. Here is what she wrote:

> 2.75 minutes = 2 minutes and 75 seconds
>
> 75 seconds = 1 minute and 15 seconds
>
> 2 + 1 = 3 minutes
>
> $3\frac{15}{60} = 3\frac{1}{4}$ minutes

What is wrong with Carole's reasoning? What could you say or do to help her convert 2.75 minutes to a fraction correctly?

17. Saajid was asked the following question on a recent quiz.

> Which of the following is between $\frac{37}{100}$ and $\frac{39}{100}$?
>
> A. 0.390
>
> B. 0.038
>
> C. 0.375
>
> D. 0.0385

Saajid chose letter B since 38 is between 37 and 39. What error did Saajid make? Which is the correct answer choice? Why?

Addition and Subtraction of Fractions and Decimals

Although fractions and decimals were not widely used in Europe until the 1600s, some rational numbers were being used hundreds and even thousands of years before that in other parts of the world. In this section, you will investigate some of the ways in which people have added and subtracted fractions and decimals, and you will develop and practice algorithms for doing this yourself.

 LESSON 3.1 Adding Fractions Around the World

 **Start It Off**

Put these fractions in order from the smallest to the largest without finding a common denominator:

$$\frac{5}{8}, \frac{36}{36}, \frac{2}{5}, \frac{15}{14}, \frac{12}{24}, \frac{19}{20}$$

Explain your reasoning.

Middle East

In Babylon, which is now part of Iraq in the Middle East, the number system was based on 60. Babylonians also used fractions in sixtieths, and sixtieths of sixtieths. This was very similar to the way we extend whole numbers in our base-ten system to tenths and hundredths. We still use the base-sixty system to tell time.

Jo Rae said she often uses a common denominator of 60 to find fractional parts of an hour. Ramon said he thinks about minutes when doing this. For example, when finding $\frac{2}{3}$ of an hour, Jo Rae multiplies both the numerator and denominator by 20 to name an equivalent fractions: $\frac{2 \cdot 20}{3 \cdot 20} = \frac{40}{60}$. Ramon said, "$\frac{1}{3}$ of an hour is 20 minutes, so $\frac{2}{3}$ of an hour is 40 minutes. 40 minutes is $\frac{40}{60}$ of an hour."

1. Write each fraction in the table as an equivalent fraction with 60 as the denominator in two ways—first by multiplying the numerator and denominator by the same number and then by thinking of the fraction as part of an hour.

Fraction	Fraction with 60 as Denominator Using Multiplication of Numerators and Denominators	Fraction as Part of an Hour with 60 as Denominator Using Minutes
$\frac{5}{6}$	$\frac{5 \cdot 10}{6 \cdot 10} = \frac{50}{60}$	$\frac{1}{6}$ hour = 10 minutes; $\frac{5}{6}$ hour = 50 minutes = $\frac{50}{60}$ hour
$\frac{2}{3}$		
$\frac{3}{4}$		
$\frac{4}{5}$		
$\frac{11}{12}$		

2. André is trying to determine how much time he needs to finish his homework. He thinks he will need a half hour for math, a third of an hour for science, three-fourths of an hour for English and three-fifths of an hour for social studies. How much time should André plan for his homework?

   a) Show how you might find the answer by changing the times to minutes.

   b) Show how you might find the answer using fractions with a common denominator.

   c) Is your answer more than 1 hour? If so, write your answer as an improper fraction and as an equivalent mixed number. For each, use a denominator of 60.

Sixtieths do not work well for all fraction problems. About 2,000 years ago in China, scholars used common fractions with any denominators. They found equivalent fractions for addition and subtraction of some rational numbers using the least common denominator (LCD) and greatest common factor (GCF). Use your skills at finding common denominators and common factors in the following.

3. Jere is making a wizard puppet. She needs $\frac{3}{4}$ yard of material for the body of the puppet, $\frac{5}{12}$ yard for a cape, and $\frac{7}{9}$ yard for a robe.

a) Estimate the amount of material Jere needs to the nearest yard.

b) Find the exact amount of material Jere needs by converting the measurements to inches. Rewrite the result as a mixed number showing the number of yards.

 **Hint**
See page 150

c) Jere said she can find the exact amount of material she needs by converting the measurements to equivalent fractions with a common denominator. To find a common denominator, she first writes several multiples of 12 (the largest number in these three denominators) and checks these to find multiples of both 4 and 9. Use her method to find a common denominator for these fractions. Add the fractions and show your work.

d) Name a different common denominator you could use. Find the amount of material needed using this denominator.

e) Write the answers to Parts c and d as mixed numbers in simplest form. Did you get the same answer using different denominators? Explain.

f) Once you wrote your fractions with a common denominator, what did you do to add them? Talk to a partner about your method.

4. Remember that there are 2 cups in a pint, 2 pints in a quart and 4 quarts in a gallon.

a) 1 gallon = _____ quarts = _____ pints = _____ cups

b) Write each of the following as a fractional part of a gallon. Show your work.

- 1 cup
- 3 cups
- $\frac{1}{2}$ pint
- 1 pint

- 3 pints
- 1 quart
- 3 quarts

c) Blake's recipe for lemonade is 1 cup of lemon juice, 3 pints of water, and $\frac{1}{2}$ pint of sugar. Write each ingredient as a fractional part of a gallon.

d) When Blake mixes his ingredients together, will he have a gallon of lemonade? Explain your method for adding these fractions.

e) Use a number line like the following to show the addition of the lemonade ingredients. Compare this to your answer to Part d.

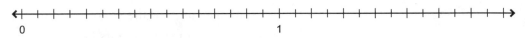

f) Double each of the lemonade ingredients. When you add these together, will they fit in a gallon jug? Explain.

America

In the 1800s, Thomas Jefferson invented a device called a pedometer that measures the distance a person walks. Today, many people use pedometers to count the steps they walk each day. Some experts suggest every person should walk 10,000 steps, or about 5 miles, each day.

Find a common denominator to solve this problem.

5. Lori walked $\frac{7}{8}$ mile from home to school. She then walked $\frac{3}{10}$ mile from school to the library. After the library, she walked $\frac{4}{5}$ mile to her friend's house and $1\frac{3}{4}$ miles home.

a) Did Lori walk more than 5 miles? Use estimation to explain.

b) Use a common denominator to determine the exact distance Lori walked. Show your work.

c) Use a different common denominator to determine this distance. Did you get the same answer? Explain.

6. **a)** Write a general rule for adding any two fractions.

    b) Give an example of your rule using two proper fractions. Use a number line to show that your rule works for these numbers.

7. Write your own word problems for the following. Show your work using your general rule and write your answer as a mixed number in simplest terms.

    a) $\frac{1}{2} + \frac{1}{6} + \frac{5}{8}$

    b) $\frac{2}{3} + \frac{1}{4} + \frac{2}{5}$

Simplify First

When you add fractions, sometimes it is easier to simplify the fractions before finding a common denominator. For example, to add $\frac{12}{24} + \frac{24}{36}$, it would be difficult to find a common denominator for twenty-fourths and thirty-sixths. If you first write $\frac{12}{24}$ as $\frac{1}{2}$ and $\frac{24}{36}$ as $\frac{2}{3}$, you then just need to find a common denominator for $\frac{1}{2}$ and $\frac{2}{3}$. Using a common denominator of 6, you can rewrite the problem as $\frac{3}{6} + \frac{4}{6}$.

Example

$$\frac{12}{24} = \frac{1}{2} = \frac{3}{6}$$
$$+ \frac{24}{36} = \frac{2}{3} = \frac{4}{6}$$
$$\frac{7}{6} = 1\frac{1}{6}$$

You could show this on a number line as: $\frac{3}{6} + \frac{4}{6} = \frac{7}{6} = 1\frac{1}{6}$

8. Revise your general rule for adding fractions to include simplifying, if you wish. If not, explain why not.

9. Add. Show your work with equations and on a number line, and simplify your answer if possible.

    a) $\frac{12}{16} + \frac{24}{36}$

    b) $\frac{12}{20} + \frac{6}{10}$

    c) $\frac{12}{36} + \frac{6}{12} + \frac{32}{48}$

Adding Mixed Numbers

You may need to add mixed numbers. For example, if you have a recipe that calls for $2\frac{1}{2}$ cups of flour and $1\frac{3}{4}$ cups of sugar, you might need to know if a 1-quart bowl is large enough to hold the mixture of flour and sugar.

10. Explain how you would find the total amount of flour and sugar:

   a) Using a number line.

   b) Using mixed numbers with common denominators.

   c) Is a 1-quart bowl large enough to hold the flour and sugar?

11. For each of the following equations, write a word problem, show your solution on a number line and by using mixed numbers with common denominators.

Equation	Word Problem	Number Line	Common Denominators
a) $1\frac{2}{3} + 2\frac{1}{2} = n$			
b) $1\frac{1}{6} + \frac{3}{4} = n$			
c) $\frac{1}{3} + 1\frac{3}{4} = n$			

⬆Wrap It Up

Explain how to find a common denominator when adding fractions with unlike denominators. Why do you find a common denominator instead of just adding the numerators and denominators together?

Write About It

1. You have $\frac{24}{36}$ yard of corduroy fabric and $\frac{12}{30}$ yard of calico fabric.

   a) Explain how to simplify each of the fractions.

   b) Use estimation to determine whether the total amount of fabric is more or less than a yard. Explain your reasoning.

   c) Once the fractions are simplified, can you add the numerators and denominators together to find the sum? Why or why not?

   d) How would you find the sum?

   e) If you have more than a yard, give your answer as an improper fraction and as a mixed number in simplest terms.

2. Maria said you could simplify $\frac{18}{30}$ by first dividing both the numerator and denominator by 2 and then dividing both the numerator and denominator by 3. Marco disagreed, saying that you must divide both the numerator and denominator by 6, because 6 is the greatest common divisor of 18 and 30. Who is right? Explain.

3. Rob said that $\frac{2}{3} + \frac{3}{4} = \frac{5}{7}$. What went wrong? Use equations and a number line to explain the correct sum to Rob.

4. Frederika needs to catch the bus for school at 7:30 am. It takes her $\frac{1}{3}$ hour to take a shower, $\frac{1}{6}$ hour to get dressed, $\frac{1}{4}$ hour to eat breakfast, $\frac{1}{12}$ hour to brush her teeth, and 5 minutes to walk to the bus stop.

   a) Estimate to determine if Frederika needs more than an hour to get ready for school.

   b) In simplest terms, what fraction of an hour does she need to get ready? Show your work.

   c) What time should Frederika get up to make sure she is not late for the bus?

5. Yesterday Deb jogged a half mile in the morning and five-sixths of a mile in the afternoon. Estimate whether Deb jogged more or less than a mile yesterday and explain your thinking. Find the exact amount of time Deb spent jogging using equations and using a number line.

6. On a recent national test on each of the following questions, fewer than half of the 13-year-old students got the correct answer. What should they have answered for each?

   a) Estimate the sum to the nearest whole number: $\frac{12}{13} + \frac{7}{8}$.

   b) What is the least common denominator for $\frac{7}{15}$ and $\frac{4}{9}$?

   c) Find the sum:

   - $2\frac{2}{5} + 5$

   - $4\frac{1}{4} + 3\frac{2}{5}$

   - $\frac{7}{15} + \frac{4}{9}$

7. Write a word problem for each of the following sums. Find the sum and write your answer in simplest terms. If the answer is greater than 1, write the sum as a mixed number. Show your work.

   a) $\frac{2}{3} + \frac{1}{6}$

   b) $3\frac{1}{3} + \frac{3}{4}$

   c) $4\frac{2}{5} + 3\frac{1}{2}$

   d) $\frac{1}{2} + \frac{2}{3} + \frac{5}{6}$

8. You know that $1 = \frac{2}{3} + \frac{2}{6}$ and $1 = \frac{3}{4} + \frac{2}{8}$.

   a) List another equation with two addends that has a sum of 1. Each addend should have a different denominator.

   b) List at least four equations that have more than two addends whose sum is 1. Each addend within each equation should have a different denominator.

9. Solve for *n*. Write your answer as a fraction or mixed number in simplest terms. Explain your solution using ideas of balance.

   a) $\frac{3}{6} + \frac{1}{3} = n + \frac{1}{3}$

   b) $n = \frac{2}{5} + \frac{1}{2}$

   c) $1\frac{1}{2} + 2\frac{3}{4} = 3 + n$

   d) $n + \frac{4}{6} = \frac{2}{3} + \frac{9}{6}$

10. Find the following sums:

    a) $\frac{1}{3} + \frac{2}{3} =$

    b) $\frac{1}{4} + \frac{2}{4} + \frac{3}{4} =$

    c) $\frac{1}{5} + \frac{2}{5} + \frac{3}{5} + \frac{4}{5} =$

    d) Write a recursive rule for the sum.

    $$\frac{1}{n} + \frac{2}{n} + \frac{3}{n} + \frac{4}{n} + \ldots + \frac{n-1}{n} =$$

    e) Write an explicit rule for the sum.

    $$\frac{1}{n} + \frac{2}{n} + \frac{3}{n} + \frac{4}{n} + \ldots + \frac{n-1}{n} =$$

 Think Beyond

Think Back

11. Cal walks at the rate of 4 miles per hour. At that rate, how long would it take him to walk each of the following distances?

    a) 2 miles

    b) 12 miles

    c) 6 miles

    d) 9 miles

12. I am thinking of an odd two-digit number. It is a multiple of 7 and the sum of its digits is 8. What is the number?

13. What are the dimensions of a square that has the same area as a rectangle that is 4 inches by 9 inches?

14. How is the Pattern I different from the others?

    Pattern I: 2, 6, 18, 54, 162 …

    Pattern II: 2, 5, 8, 11, 14 …

    Pattern III: 5, 10, 15, 20, 25 …

    Pattern IV: 4, 9, 14, 19, 24 …

15. Can you find two consecutive numbers with an even sum?

    Why or why not?

Additional Addition Around the World

Start It Off

The hexagon has an area of 1 unit.

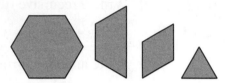

1. What is the area of each of the other shapes?

2. Using copies of these shapes, how many different ways can you make one whole hexagon? Write an equation for each. For example, you might use the trapezoid and three triangles and write $\frac{1}{2} + \frac{3}{6} = 1$.

Out of Africa

Over 6,000 years ago in Egypt, only unit fractions were used. Recall that unit fractions are fractions with a numerator of 1. Egyptians wrote any fraction that was not already a unit fraction as a sum of unit fractions $\frac{1}{a} + \frac{1}{b} + \frac{1}{c} + \dots$ where a, b and c had *different* values. For example, $\frac{2}{3}$ might be written as $\frac{1}{2} + \frac{1}{6}$ and $\frac{3}{4}$ as $\frac{1}{2} + \frac{1}{4}$.

1. Write each of the following as the sum of two or more different unit fractions. Check using equivalent fractions with a common denominator.

   a) $\frac{3}{8}$

   b) $\frac{5}{6}$

   c) $\frac{7}{12}$

   Unit fractions can also be written as the sum of other unit fractions. Study the following pattern:

   - $\frac{1}{2} = \frac{1}{3} + \frac{1}{6}$
   - $\frac{1}{4} = \frac{1}{6} + \frac{1}{12}$
   - $\frac{1}{6} = \frac{1}{9} + \frac{1}{18}$

2. Write $\frac{1}{8}$ as the sum of two different unit fractions.

3. Write an explicit rule for finding two unit fractions with a sum of $\frac{1}{n}$, where n is any even number. Use your rule to find two unit fractions with a sum of $\frac{1}{50}$. You may use your calculator to try out your rule on other unit fractions.

Worldwide Magic

MATHEMATICALLY
SPEAKING

▶ magic square

Magic squares, ancient mathematical puzzles, have been known for nearly 4,000 years. The oldest have been found in China, but magic squares thousands of years old have also been found in Africa, the Middle East, India and Europe. Artists in Germany and Spain included magic squares in their paintings. Benjamin Franklin created a 16×16 magic square that he called, "the most magically magical of any square ever made by any magician." An ancient Chinese legend tells of a magic puzzle on the back of a turtle named Lo Shu. The puzzle was a pattern of dots as shown below. Study the pattern in the dots to see if you can solve the puzzle.

? Hint
See page 150

Magic squares are usually made up of whole numbers, but they can use fractions too. To be "magic," the numbers in each row, column and diagonal must have the same sum. This value is called a magic sum.

4. Study this partially completed magic square.

$\frac{1}{6}$		$\frac{5}{9}$
$\frac{8}{9}$	$\frac{1}{2}$	
$\frac{4}{9}$		$\frac{5}{6}$

a) What is the magic sum?

b) Complete the square using fractions in simplest form.

5. Complete the following. In Part a, the magic sum is $1\frac{2}{3}$. Determine the magic sum in Part b and then complete the square.

a) Magic Sum $= 1\frac{2}{3}$

$\frac{2}{3}$		$\frac{8}{9}$
	$\frac{5}{9}$	

b) Magic Sum = _____

	0	$\frac{15}{8}$
	$\frac{3}{2}$	
	$\frac{3}{1}$	

MATHEMATICALLY SPEAKING

▶ magic triangle

6. In a magic triangle, the sum of the numbers along each of the three sides is the same. Put the following fractions in the circles below to make this a magic triangle with a sum of 1 along each side:

$$\frac{1}{12}, \frac{1}{6}, \frac{1}{4}, \frac{1}{3}, \frac{5}{12}, \frac{1}{2}$$

Magic Sum $= 1$

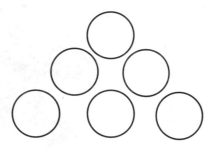

Wrap It Up

Choose either addition of unit fractions, fraction magic squares or fraction magic triangles, and discuss three patterns that you noticed. Be prepared to share your observations with the class.

MATHEMATICALLY SPEAKING

▶ magic square

▶ magic triangle

LESSON
3.2   SECTION 3
On Your Own

MATERIALS LIST
▶ Lesson Guide 3.2:
   On Your Own

 **Write About It**

1. Recall that the pattern on Lo Shu's back formed this magic square.

8	3	4
1	5	9
6	7	2

Explain how you might use this pattern to create your own magic square using fractions and mixed numbers. Show your completed magic square and give the magic sum.

 **Hint**
See page 150

2. Choose four different one-digit numbers. Place them in the squares below to make each of the following statements true. You may use a different four numbers each time.

$$\frac{\square}{\square} + \frac{\square}{\square} = $$

a) two addends with a sum of 1

b) two addends with the greatest possible sum

c) two addends with the least possible sum

d) Make up your own problem. Include the solution.

e) Check your addition using a calculator. Do you always get the same answer when you use paper and a pencil and when you use a calculator? Explain.

Think Beyond

3) Use six different one-digit numbers in the following squares.

$$\frac{\square}{\square} + \frac{\square}{\square} + \frac{\square}{\square} = $$

Find:

a) three addends with a sum of 1

b) three addends with the greatest possible sum

c) three addends with the least possible sum

d) Make up your own problem. Include the solution.

4. Complete each magic square.

a) Magic Sum = 1

	$\frac{3}{15}$	
	$\frac{1}{3}$	
$\frac{2}{15}$		

b) Magic Sum = $11\frac{1}{4}$

6		3
$\frac{9}{2}$		$1\frac{1}{2}$

5. Put the following fractions in the circles below to make a magic triangle: $\frac{1}{12}, \frac{1}{6}, \frac{1}{4}, \frac{1}{3}, \frac{5}{12}, \frac{1}{2}$

Magic Sum = $\frac{3}{4}$

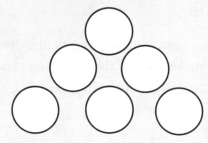

**Think Beyond**

6. Three sons asked the Grand Vizier in Egypt to help them split up the horses their father left them in his will. The will said that the oldest son should get half the horses, the next son should get one-fourth of the horses, and the youngest should get one-fifth of the horses. The father left them 19 horses. The sons could not figure out how many horses each of them should get. The Vizier thought for a moment and then added his own horse to make a total of 20 horses. The sons then each took their fractional amounts and the Vizier was left with his own horse. Explain how this could work.

Think Beyond

7. Look at the following pattern:

- $\frac{1}{3} = \frac{1}{6} + \frac{1}{9} + \frac{1}{18}$

- $\frac{1}{5} = \frac{1}{10} + \frac{1}{15} + \frac{1}{30}$

- $\frac{1}{7} = \frac{1}{14} + \frac{1}{21} + \frac{1}{42}$

a) Following the pattern, list three different unit fractions with a sum of $\frac{1}{9}$.

b) Check your sum using a common denominator. Simplify the answer.

c) Write an explicit rule for finding three unit fractions with a sum of $\frac{1}{n}$ where n is any odd number. Use your rule to find three unit fractions with a sum of $\frac{1}{21}$. If you have a fraction key on your calculator, you may use your calculator to test your rule on other unit fractions.

Think Back

8. The German artist Albrecht Durer included this magic square in his painting *Melancholia* in 1514.

Think Beyond

a) What is the magic sum?

b) Where can you find the magic sum besides as the sum of each row, column and diagonal?

9. Can you find two consecutive numbers with an odd product? Why or why not?

10. Apples are 3 for $4 and oranges are 10 for $5. How much should you pay for 2 apples and 5 oranges?

11. List the following:

a) three factors of 15

b) three multiples of 15

c) one number that is both a factor of 15 and a multiple of 15

12. You might use four 4s to make the number 1 like this: $\frac{44}{44}$. You might use four 4s to make the number 8 like this: $(4 \cdot 4) - (4 + 4)$. How many other numbers less than 10 can you make using four 4s and any of the operations?

LESSON 3.3 Dazzling Decimals

➡ Start It Off

1. Factor 20 and 35 into prime factors.

   20 = _____ 35 = _____

2. Put each of the prime factors of 20 and 35 in the Venn diagram below. What should go in the intersection?

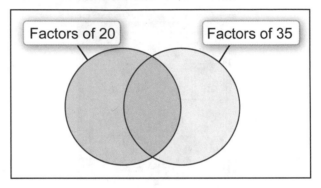

Factors of 20   Factors of 35

3. What is the greatest common factor of 20 and 35? How does this relate to the Venn diagram? How can you use this to simplify $\frac{20}{35}$?

4. Factor 24 and 36 into prime factors and place each of the prime factors in the following Venn diagram. What is the greatest common factor of 24 and 36? How does this relate to the Venn diagram? How can you use this to simplify $\frac{24}{36}$?

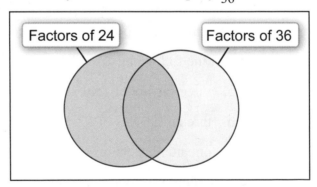

Factors of 24   Factors of 36

5. Explain how you might use a Venn diagram to find the greatest common factor of any pair of numbers. Choose a new pair of numbers to illustrate your explanation.

The Nature Walk

Lewis and Clark Middle School students are planning a nature walk behind their school. The sixth grade students are in charge of deciding what to plant along a 1-kilometer walkway. Leroy has suggested that they plant wildflowers along the first 0.7 kilometer, roses along the next 0.25 kilometer, and herbs along the final part.

Tad said that Leroy's plan would mean that they would have to plant too many herbs. He said that $25 + 7 = 32$, so $0.25 + 0.7$ would only be 0.32 kilometer. Leroy said that could not be right since 0.32 is less than 0.7.

1. Who was right, Tad or Leroy? Discuss your reasoning with a partner.

2. Using Leroy's plan, Colleen said she could figure out the length of the walkway that should be planted in wildflowers and roses by thinking about money. She said that 0.7 is like 7 dimes and 0.25 is like a quarter. Explain how Colleen might use money to find the total length of the walkway that should be planted in wildflowers and roses.

3. How might Marissa determine the total length to be planted in roses and wildflowers with Leroy's plan using fractions with a common denominator of 100?

4. Doug said that he sums a decimal that has tenths and another that has hundredths by writing both as hundredths before adding. Use Doug's method to add 0.7 and 0.25.

5. Did you get the same answer using Colleen's method, Marissa's method and Doug's method? Choose your favorite method to find the sum of each of the following.

    a) $0.32 + 0.5$

    b) $0.2 + 0.45 + 0.12$

    c) $0.18 + 0.4 + 0.42$

    d) Do any of these expressions have a sum of 1? Write three other expressions that have a sum of 1. Each expressions should have either two or three addends.

    e) Explain how you might add decimals if at least one of the addends has a number in the thousandths place. Use $0.415 + 0.2 + 0.38$ as an example.

Thinking about place value is very useful in estimating decimal sums.

6. Use estimation to answer the following. Compare your responses to a partner's and discuss your reasoning.

   a) $0.2 + 0.0005 + 0.06 = n$. Is n closer to 0.2 or 0.3?

   b) $2.15 + 3.8 + 4.00008 = m$. Is m greater or less than 10?

Trail Mix

To pay for the nature walk, the class has decided to make and sell Lewis and Clark Trail Mix. They plan to make the mix in 1-kilogram (kg) packages. They will begin with the following recipe:

$$0.2 \text{ kg peanuts}$$
$$0.15 \text{ kg raisins}$$
$$0.45 \text{ kg pretzel sticks}$$
$$0.1 \text{ kg granola}$$

7. This is not quite enough to make 1 kg of trail mix.

   a) How much more will the students need to add to make 1 kg? Explain your thinking.

   b) Half the class wants to add dried cranberries and the other half wants to add chocolate chips. They decide to add both. How much of each should they add to make 1 kg of mix total? Is there more than one way to do this? If so, list other ways.

   c) What percent of the total 1 kg of trail mix is made up of each ingredient? Do your percents add to 100%?

8. Keli thinks that there are too many pretzel sticks in the mix. She wants to use $\frac{1}{4}$ kg of pretzel sticks and 0.2 kg of sesame sticks. If the amounts of other ingredients stay the same, will the total weight of the mixture stay the same? Explain.

9. Design your own trail mix that has a total weight of 1 kg. You may use any ingredients you like. List their weights using decimals. Show your work to prove that your mix has a total weight of 1 kg.

Troy wants to make trail mix at home. He tells his mom that he wants to make 1 kilogram of mix, but he is not sure how to add decimals to make sure he has the right amount of ingredients. Troy's mom suggests that he add the decimals by writing them in a column with their decimal points lined up. For example, to add 0.235 + 0.4 + 0.32, Troy could write:

```
  0.235
  0.4
+ 0.32
```

Troy thinks this looks very confusing. Troy's sister suggests that Troy write all the decimals as thousandths before adding them.

10. **a)** Estimate. Is 0.235 + 0.4 + 0.32 more or less than 1? Explain your reasoning.

   b) Check your estimate by writing each of the decimals as thousandths and then writing them in a column with their decimal points lined up. Add your numbers, keeping the place value of the numbers in mind, adding thousandths to thousandths, hundredths to hundredths, and tenths to tenths. Was your estimate correct?

11. Describe a method you could use to add any decimals. Give at least three examples using decimals greater than and less than 1 with different numbers of decimal places.

12. List the weights of at least three ingredients that Troy might use to make 1 kg of trail mix. The weight of at least one of the ingredients should be in thousandths of a kilogram and the weight of at at least one other should be in tenths of a kilogram. Show that the total weight of the mix is exactly 1 kg.

Wrap It Up

Some math books tell you to add decimals by putting them in a column with the decimal points lined up. As a student mathematician, write directions for another student explaining why this works using what you know about equivalent decimals.

LESSON
3.3 SECTION 3

On Your Own

MATERIALS LIST

▶ Lesson Guide 3.3:
On Your Own

 **Write About It**

1. Dion said that to add decimals, he first finds equivalent decimals with the same number of decimal places. He then adds the numbers by writing them in a column in which the decimal points are lined up. Shonna said that she adds decimals by rewriting them as fractions and then finding a common denominator.

   a) Show how Dion and Shonna would each add $0.2 + 0.357 + 0.16$.

   b) Which method do you prefer? Why?

2. You want to plant roses, wildflowers and herbs along a 1-kilometer walkway. List two different ways you might do this. Use your preferred method of addition to show that you have plants along the entire walkway.

3. Estimate each sum to the nearest hundredth:

   a) $0.03 + 0.0003 + 0.000003$

   b) $5.2 + 0.63 + 7.000000007$

4. Cassandra said that $0.4 + 3 = 0.7$. Was she right? Explain.

5. Luke said that four-tenths plus seven-tenths is eleven-tenths.

   a) Add four-tenths and seven-tenths using fractions and write the sum as an improper fraction and as a mixed number.

   b) Add four-tenths and seven-tenths using decimals.

   c) Luke wrote eleven-tenths as 0.11. Marc said that eleven-tenths should be written as 1.1. Who was correct? Explain.

6. You have the following ingredients:

   - 0.25 kg peanuts
   - 0.3 kg cashews
   - 0.125 kg pretzels
   - 0.375 kg sesame sticks

   - 0.5 kg cereal
   - 0.1 kg dried cherries
   - 0.15 kg raisins
   - 0.05 kg dried cranberries

   a) List two different ways to use these ingredients to make exactly 1 kilogram of trail mix. You must use all of each ingredient that you choose for each mix, but you do not need to use every ingredient listed.

b) Use equivalent decimals to show that your first mix has exactly 1 kilogram of ingredients.

c) Use equivalent fractions to show that your second mix has exactly 1 kilogram of ingredients.

7. Liz wrote

$$
\begin{array}{r}
6.32 \\
4.3 \\
+\ 0.113 \\
\hline
0.788
\end{array}
$$

Is Liz correct? Why or why not?

8. Study the following patterns and write the next three numbers in each sequence.

a) 0.12, 0.24, 0.36, 0.48, _____, _____, _____

b) 0.1, 0.3, 0.5, 0.7, _____, _____, _____

c) 0.2, 0.25, 0.3, 0.35, _____, _____, _____

d) Write an explicit rule for the nth term in each sequence.

9. Jocelyn is putting coins in a vending machine to buy a bag of cheese crackers that costs $1.25.

a) Copy and complete the following chart to list the total amount shown on the vending machine after she puts in each coin.

Coin	Total Amount in Vending Machine
Nickel	$0.05
Dime	$0.15
Quarter	
Dime	
Quarter	

b) How much more money does Jocelyn need to put into the vending machine to buy the cheese crackers?

c) How might Jocelyn buy the crackers using two more coins?

d) How might Jocelyn buy the crackers using four more coins?

10. Mrs. Jeffrey baked some cookies. She gave half of them to her neighbor and $\frac{1}{3}$ to her son. She had 6 cookies left. How many cookies had she baked?

**Think
Back**

11. a) Plot the following points on a coordinate graph:

A (3, 5)
B (7, 5)
C (3, 1)

b) If A, B and C are three vertices of a square, what are the coordinates of point D, the fourth vertex?

12. a) Copy then shade $\frac{2}{5}$ of the square below.

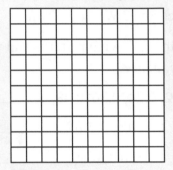

b) What percent of the square is shaded? Write this as a percent and as a decimal.

13. The Spirit Club sells T-shirts in red or blue, the school colors. The T-shirts come in small, medium, large and extra large. How many different types of T-shirts does the Spirit Club sell? List them.

14. a) Which of the following nets could be folded into a cube?

    i.   **ii.**   **iii.**

  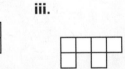

b) Draw two other nets that could be folded into a cube.

15. In each set, which number does not belong with the others? Why?

a) 75%   0.75   7.5 $\frac{6}{8}$

b) $\frac{2}{3}$ 0.6 $\frac{4}{6}$ $66\frac{2}{3}$%

c)   0.4   0.40 $\frac{1}{4}$ $\frac{2}{5}$

Adding It All Together

➡️ Start It Off

1. Factor 20 and 35 into prime factors.

    20 = _____ 35 = _____

2. Put each of the prime factors of 20 and 35 in the Venn diagram below.

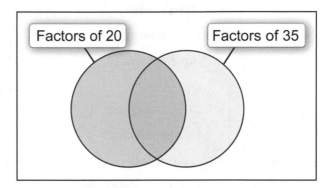

Factors of 20   Factors of 35

3. What is the least common multiple of 20 and 35? Factor this number into prime factors. How does this relate to the Venn diagram? How would you use this to find the sum $\frac{3}{20} + \frac{4}{35}$?

4. Factor 24 and 36 into prime factors and place each of the prime factors in the following Venn diagram. What is the least common multiple of 24 and 36? Factor this number into prime factors. How does this relate to the Venn diagram? How would you use this to find the sum $\frac{5}{24} + \frac{7}{36}$?

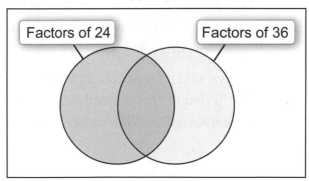

Factors of 24   Factors of 36

5. Explain how you might use a Venn diagram to find the least common multiple of any pair of numbers. Choose a new pair of numbers to illustrate your explanation.

More Trail Mix

Each student in Mr. Carlson's sixth grade class at Lewis and Clark Middle School brought something different to make trail mix. They each weighed what they brought and put it in a small marked bag. One of the scales they used showed decimal parts of a kilogram and the other showed fractional parts of a kilogram. They listed the ingredients that they brought.

Student Trail Mix Ingredients	
• 0.3 kg dried cherries	• 0.1 kg sunflower seeds
• 0.08 kg raisins	• 0.05 kg coconut
• 0.15 kg peanuts	• $\frac{2}{10}$ kg sesame sticks
• $\frac{3}{20}$ kg cashews	• 0.25 kg dates
• $\frac{1}{4}$ kg M&M's®	• $\frac{1}{3}$ kg almonds
• 0.21 kg oat cereal	• 0.35 kg cornflakes
• $\frac{1}{8}$ kg banana chips	• 0.025 kg potato sticks
• $\frac{3}{10}$ kg pretzels	• 0.075 kg dried cranberries
• 0.2 kg chocolate chips	• $\frac{2}{5}$ kg miniature marshmallows
• $\frac{3}{8}$ kg popcorn	• 0.3 kg small cheese crackers
• 0.150 kg walnuts	• 0.205 kg peanut butter chips
• 0.015 kg dried apricots	• $\frac{1}{10}$ kg granola
	• 0.075 kg dried cranberries

Mr. Carlson challenged the class to determine different mixes that would make exactly 1 kilogram of trail mix. He said that they could use as many different ingredients as they wanted, but they had to use all of whatever they chose. For example, if they wanted to use the miniature marshmallows, they had to use all $\frac{2}{5}$ kilogram. They could not use only $\frac{1}{5}$ kilogram.

Jocelyn said that she loved cashews and dried cherries but she did not know how to find their combined weight because the dried cherries were weighed using decimals and the cashews were weighed using fractions.

1. Emily says that she should write 0.3 as a fraction and add the two fractions. Nasha says that she should write $\frac{3}{20}$ as a decimal and then add the two decimals.

   a) Estimate. Is the total more or less than $\frac{1}{2}$ kilogram? Explain.

   b) Use Emily's method to add $\frac{3}{20} + 0.3$.

   c) Use Nasha's method to add $\frac{3}{20} + 0.3$.

   d) Did you get the same answer each time? Was your estimate correct?

   e) How much would you need to add to make 1 kilogram of trail mix?

2. With a partner, make up your own trail mix that weighs exactly 1 kilogram using these ingredients. You may use as many different ingredients as you want, but you must use all of each ingredient you choose.

Mr. Carlson's class decided to make a card game about their trail mix amounts. They called it **Thumbs Up**.

 · · · · · **Thumbs Up** · · · · ·

Players: Whole Class
Materials: Trail Mix cards
Goal: To estimate the sum of fractions and decimals

DIRECTIONS:

Two leaders each choose a card and announce the amounts on the cards to the class. Each student mentally adds the two amounts. If the total is more than $\frac{1}{2}$ kilogram, each student puts one thumb up. If the total is less than $\frac{1}{2}$ kilogram, each student puts one thumb down. If the total is exactly $\frac{1}{2}$ kilogram, each student puts one thumb sideways. The leaders then add the two amounts on the board to determine the correct answer. Each student with the correct answer receives 1 point. After five rounds, two new leaders are then chosen from among the students with the highest scores and play continues.

 **Think Beyond**

Play with three or four cards. Decide if the total is more than, less than or equal to 1 kilogram.

3. Scott and Eva picked 0.3 kg of dried cherries and 0.21 kg oat cereal. Scott said that this is less than $\frac{1}{2}$ kilogram because $21 + 3 = 24$ and 0.24 is less than one-half. Was Scott correct? Explain.

4. Gabe and Ceci chose $\frac{2}{10}$ kg of sesame sticks and $\frac{2}{5}$ kg of miniature marshmallows. Ceci said that $\frac{2}{5} + \frac{2}{10} = \frac{4}{15}$ and that $\frac{4}{15} < \frac{1}{2}$. Was Ceci correct? Explain.

5. Marion and Cinnamon want to choose two cards that add to exactly $\frac{1}{2}$ kg. Name two different ways that they might do this.

Lots More Trail Mix

The class decided that they wanted to use a mix of raisins, peanuts, pretzels, and peanut butter chips. They also decided that 1-kilogram packages were too large to sell, so they chose to sell 1-pound packages instead. They decided to begin with 20 pounds of trail mix for their first sales.

At the organic food store, they found ingredients that each come in two different size of packages.

Raisins	3.5 pounds or $4\frac{2}{5}$ pounds
Peanuts	7.375 pounds or $4\frac{1}{2}$ pounds
Pretzels	6.25 pounds or $5\frac{5}{8}$ pounds
Peanut butter chips	2.6 pounds or $5\frac{3}{4}$ pounds

6. Lauren says that they should buy $4\frac{2}{5}$ pounds of raisins, 7.375 pounds of peanuts, 6.25 pounds of pretzels and 2.6 pounds of peanut butter chips.

   a) Lauren said that she knew that this was enough because she added all the whole numbers together ($4 + 7 + 6 + 2 = 19$). She said that it was obvious that the fractions and decimals would add to more than the 1 pound she still needed. Is Lauren correct?

   b) Find the total weight of Lauren's ingredients using decimals. Check by using fractions.

   c) Can you come up with a trail mix that is closer to 20 pounds that uses all four ingredients? List your ingredients and prove that the weight of your mixture is closer to 20 pounds than the weight of Lauren's mixture. Be sure it does not weigh less than 20 pounds. Show your work using decimals and using fractions or mixed numbers.

Wrap It Up

Sometimes you have to add a combination of fractions and decimals. You can do this by first converting all of the numbers to decimals or all to fractions or mixed numbers, and then adding them. Which do you prefer? Why?

On Your Own

Write About It

1. Deedra said that to add 14.375 and $3\frac{5}{8}$, she would write both numbers as mixed numbers, add the whole numbers, and finally add the fractions. Paul said that he would prefer to write both numbers as decimals and then add those numbers together.

   a) Add the numbers using both Deedra's method and Paul's method.

   b) Which method do you prefer? Why?

2. Suzy is mixing paint for one wall of her room. She has $\frac{5}{8}$ quart of blue paint, 0.25 quart of yellow paint and 0.15 quart of white. She needs at least 1 quart of paint. Does she have enough? Explain.

For Questions 3–6, use the following amounts of each ingredient.

Dried cherries: 0.25 pound	Peanuts: $\frac{5}{8}$ pound	Cashews: 0.4 pound	Pretzels: $\frac{7}{20}$ pound
Cheese crackers: 0.375 pound	Sunflower seeds: $\frac{2}{5}$ pound	Chocolate chips: 0.30 pound	Granola: 0.05 pound

3. **a)** Add $\frac{1}{5}$ pound of raisins to the cashews and dried cherries. Find the total weight of the mixture using fractions.

   b) Add $\frac{1}{5}$ pound of raisins to the cashews and dried cherries. Find the total weight of the mixture using decimals.

   c) What weight is still needed to make 1 pound of trail mix? Is there a single ingredient on the list that you might add to make the total weight 1 pound? Explain.

4. Sal said that he could make exactly 1 pound using only peanuts and cheese crackers. Was he correct? Explain using fractions and decimals.

5. Pat wanted to use pretzels, sunflower seeds and one additional ingredient. What should she choose for the additional ingredient to make exactly 1 pound of mix?

Think Beyond

6. Jason wants to use exactly four ingredients to make exactly 1 pound of trail mix. What four ingredients should he choose? Can he do this in two different ways?

7. Marissa wants to make $\frac{1}{3}$ cup of fruit salad. She has $\frac{2}{5}$ cup of bananas and $\frac{1}{4}$ cup of apples. She adds $\frac{2}{5} + \frac{1}{4} = \frac{3}{9}$. She knows that she can simplify $\frac{3}{9}$ to $\frac{1}{3}$. She says that this will make exactly $\frac{1}{3}$ cup of fruit salad. Is Marissa right? Explain.

8. Lacy wants to walk a mile each day. One day she walked 0.76 mile in the morning and 0.24 mile in the afternoon, and said she walked exactly 1 mile. Sam says that this was only 0.100 mile, which is much less than 1 mile. Who is right? Explain.

9. Ms. Jamison has to drive $3\frac{1}{4}$ miles to the grocery store, 5.25 miles to pick up her son at school, 2.85 miles to take him to soccer, and then $8\frac{5}{8}$ miles back home. She has enough gas to drive 20 miles. Will she have enough gas to run her errands and get home? Explain.

10. On a recent national test, about half of the 13-year-old students answered the following question correctly. What should the answer be? Show your work.

    A cake recipe calls for $2\frac{1}{4}$ cups of sugar for the cake and $1\frac{1}{2}$ cups of sugar for the frosting. How much sugar is needed altogether?

11. Solve for n.

    a) $3\frac{1}{2} + 4.25 = 4\frac{1}{n} + 3.5$

    b) $3.2 + n = 7 + \frac{1}{2}$

    c) $n + 6 = 2.3 + 4\frac{1}{2}$

12. a) Draw a Venn diagram to show the prime factors of 36 and 60.

    b) Show how you would use the factors in the intersection to simplify the fraction $\frac{36}{60}$.

    c) Show how you would use the factors in the union to find a common denominator for $\frac{1}{60} + \frac{1}{36}$.

13. Springfield had rain or clouds 231 days last year. Approximately what percent of the days did not have rain or clouds?

  A. 33%   **C.** 25%

  B. 66%   **D.** 70%

14. a) Estimate the fractional part of the figure that is shaded and explain your reasoning.

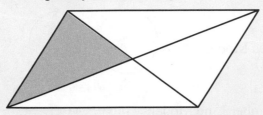

  b) What percent of the figure is shaded?

  c) What is the geometric name of the figure?

15. Draw the next two figures in the pattern:

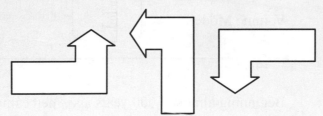

16. In each set, which number does not belong with the others? Why?

  a) 25%, 0.25, $\frac{25}{10}$, $\frac{6}{24}$

  b) $\frac{3}{5}$, 0.6, 6%, $\frac{60}{100}$

  c) 0.3, 0.30, $\frac{1}{3}$, $\frac{3}{10}$

17. For each of the following, state whether it is always true, sometimes true or never true. Give an example for each.

  a) The sum of an odd number and an even number is an odd number.

  b) The product of two odd numbers is even.

  c) When you divide an even number by an odd number, the quotient will have a remainder.

  d) A multiple of 6 is also a multiple of 3.

  e) A multiple of 3 is also a multiple of 6.

The Miniature Olympiad: Subtracting Fractions

→ Start It Off

A recipe calls for $3\frac{1}{4}$ cups of flour, but you only have $1\frac{3}{8}$ cups of flour. Choose one of the following models and use it to show how you could determine how much more flour you need. Compare your results to those of a classmate who used a different model.

Area Model:

Number Line Model:

Volume Model:

Beginning almost 3,000 years ago, men came to Olympia, Greece every four years to compete against each other in an athletic festival known today as the Olympics. At first, the men only competed against each other in a short race, but gradually longer races, javelin throwing, discus throwing, a long jump, wrestling, boxing and chariot racing were added.

The Javelin Throw

Students at Eastside Middle School decided to hold their own mini-Olympiad. Instead of throwing a javelin, they decided to throw straws. The table shows the results.

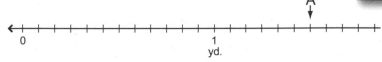

1. **a)** Mark each person's throw on a number line like the one above. Use their first initial.

   b) Which two throws are the farthest apart? What is the distance between them?

   c) How much farther did Jacob throw the straw than Darius? Show your work and write your answer in simplest form.

   d) Name two throws that are $\frac{1}{2}$ yd. apart. Can you do this in more than one way? Explain. Show these distances on the number line as part of your explanation.

   e) Make up your own questions about the straw javelin throw and share with a partner. If your class has held their own mini-Olympiad, use those results for your questions.

2. Kayella threw her straw $2\frac{5}{6}$ feet and Jackson threw his $4\frac{1}{2}$ feet. These might be shown on the number line as:

   a) What is the distance between Kayella's throw and Jackson's throw? How might you use the number line to determine this?

   b) Martin threw the straw 3 feet. Ned threw it $4\frac{2}{3}$ feet. Show these distances on a number line.

   c) How does the distance between Martin's and Ned's throws compare to the distance between Kayella's and Jackson's throws? How is this related to the number lines?

SCORECARD

Karl	$4\frac{1}{6}$ ft.
Omar	$3\frac{5}{3}$ ft.
Pablo	$1\frac{2}{3}$ ft.
Lisa	$\frac{16}{18}$ ft.
Ray	$3\frac{3}{4}$ ft.
Moesha	$2\frac{1}{2}$ ft.
SuElla	$2\frac{5}{6}$ ft.
Nela	$3\frac{12}{18}$ ft.
Tim	$3\frac{3}{6}$ ft.
Wie	$4\frac{1}{3}$ ft.

Next, the students held a paper plate discus throw competition. The table shows the results. Note that not every distance is in a simplified form.

3. Wie said that she had the longest throw because only she and Karl had throws longer than 4 feet, and $\frac{1}{3}$ is greater than $\frac{1}{6}$. Omar said that his throw was the longest of all.

 a) Draw a number line and mark points showing the distances for Wie, Karl and Omar. Label each point with the student's initial.

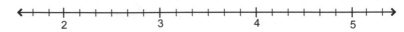

 b) Who had the longest throw? Write the distance for this throw as a mixed number in simplified form.

 c) How much farther than Wie's throw was the longest throw?

Sometimes it is easier to write and solve equations than to draw a number line or use another model. Sometimes a different model makes it easier to make sense of the numbers. If you want to subtract $4\frac{2}{3} - 4\frac{1}{3}$, you can just think $4 - 4 = 0$ and $\frac{2}{3} - \frac{1}{3} = \frac{1}{3}$. You also might draw a picture like the following:

MATHEMATICALLY SPEAKING

▶ minuend
▶ subtrahend

Note that in a subtraction problem, the first number is called the minuend and the second number, the number that is being subtracted, is called the subtrahend. In this case, the $4\frac{2}{3}$ is the minuend and the $4\frac{1}{3}$ is the subtrahend.

To subtract $3 - \frac{7}{8}$, you might think $\frac{7}{8}$ is $\frac{1}{8}$ away from 1, and 3 is 2 away from 1, so $3 - \frac{7}{8} = 2\frac{1}{8}$. Not all subtraction problems are this simple, though.

On a number line, the distance between Ray's throw at $3\frac{3}{4}$ feet and SuElla's throw at $2\frac{5}{6}$ feet might look like this:

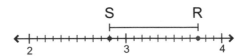

4. Talk to a partner about how you might determine the distance between Ray's throw and SuElla's throw without using a number line. You may use another model such an area model or a measuring cup. You should also do this using equations only. Be prepared to discuss your thinking with the class. There are many ways to do this.

5. SuElla said that she started with $2\frac{5}{6}$ and added $\frac{1}{6}$ more to get to 3. From 3 to $3\frac{3}{4}$ is $\frac{3}{4}$. SuElla then said that she just needed to add: $\frac{1}{6} + \frac{3}{4} = \frac{2}{12} + \frac{9}{12} = \frac{11}{12}$. SuElla calls her method "adding up."

   a) How does SuElla's "adding up" method relate to the equation $3\frac{3}{4} - 2\frac{5}{6} = n$?

   b) Look at the number line on page 118. What is the value of each small section on the number line? What are the two endpoints of the line segment above the number line?

   c) Think about sliding the line segment above the number line to the right by $\frac{1}{6}$ of a unit.

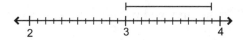

   What are the new endpoints of the line segment? What new subtraction problem does this suggest? How does this relate to SuElla's method of "adding up"?

   d) Try SuElla's method on the following. Use equations and number lines. Be prepared to discuss your method with the class.

   - $2\frac{1}{4} - 1\frac{1}{2}$
   - $3\frac{1}{3} - 1\frac{2}{3}$
   - $3\frac{2}{5} - 1\frac{7}{10}$

6. Another way to subtract fractions uses regrouping. For the problem $4\frac{1}{3} - 1\frac{2}{3}$, you might first look at the fractions. Since $\frac{2}{3}$ is greater than $\frac{1}{3}$, you could regroup one whole as $\frac{3}{3}$. Study the following:

$$4\frac{1}{3} = 3\frac{4}{3}$$
$$-\ 1\frac{2}{3} = -1\frac{2}{3}$$
$$\rule{3cm}{0.4pt}$$
$$2\frac{2}{3}$$

   Compare this regrouping algorithm to your solution using the adding up algorithm.

7. How would you use regrouping for $3\frac{3}{4} - 2\frac{5}{6}$?

a) Think about common denominators and show your work.

$$3\frac{3}{4}$$
$$-\ 2\frac{5}{6}$$
_____

b) Carla was confused by the regrouping method. She thought $3\frac{9}{12}$ should be regrouped as $2\frac{19}{12}$? Explain to Carla why you regroup $3\frac{9}{12}$ as $2\frac{21}{12}$ instead of $2\frac{19}{12}$.

c) Use regrouping for $3\frac{2}{5} - 1\frac{7}{10}$. Show your work.

d) Do you prefer regrouping or adding up? Why?

8. Solve each of the following using the method of your choice and the paper plate discus throw data above. Show your work.

a) What was the distance between the longest and the shortest throw?

b) Name two other throws that were more than 2 feet apart. What was the distance between these two throws?

c) Which two throws were the closest to each other? What is the distance between them?

d) Karl and Pablo were on one team and Wie and Lisa were on another. Each pair's distances were totaled for their team's score. Which team won? What is the difference between the teams' scores?

e) Write your own subtraction word problem about the paper plate discus throws. Trade with a classmate and solve each other's problem. Do you agree on the solutions?

⬆W rap It Up

Sometimes the answer to a subtraction problem is found mentally, sometimes it is determined by using a model such as an area model or a number line, and sometimes it is found by computing with numbers. Show how you might use mental computation, a number line, a regrouping algorithm, or an adding up algorithm to find $6\frac{1}{4} - 4\frac{5}{8}$.

MATHEMATICALLY SPEAKING

▶ minuend

▶ subtrahend

Write About It

1. Jake threw the paper plate discus $3\frac{5}{6}$ feet and Jaela threw it $2\frac{11}{12}$ feet. How much farther did Jake throw the discus than Jaela? Explain how you would find this distance using:

   a) mental math

   b) a model (number line, area model or other)

   c) adding up algorithm

   d) regrouping algorithm

2. Jorge is reading a book. He read $\frac{2}{7}$ of the book on Monday and $\frac{1}{4}$ of the book on Tuesday. What portion of the book does he still need to read?

3. Find the value of $1\frac{1}{4} - \frac{3}{8} + \frac{1}{2}$. Express your answer in simplest form.

4. Jeremy lives $1\frac{1}{4}$ miles from school, JoElla lives $\frac{9}{8}$ miles from school, and Lou lives $1\frac{5}{12}$ miles from school.

   a) Who lives the farthest from school?

   b) How much farther does the farthest person live from school than the closest person?

5. In the morning, Tabitha walked $\frac{3}{8}$ mile, rested and then walked another $\frac{1}{2}$ mile. In the afternoon, she walked $1\frac{1}{4}$ miles. Did she walk more in the morning or in the afternoon? How much more?

6. Carlos wants to use the regrouping algorithm to solve $4\frac{1}{2} - 2\frac{7}{12}$.

   a) Does Carlos need to regroup? Explain.

   b) Carlos knows that $4\frac{1}{2} = 4\frac{6}{12}$. Why has he chosen to rename $\frac{1}{2}$ as $\frac{6}{12}$?

   c) Carlos says that $4\frac{6}{12} = 3\frac{16}{12}$. Is this correct? Explain.

   d) Complete the subtraction using the regrouping method.

   e) Explain how you would do this problem using the adding up method.

7. Ray said that he could subtract mixed numbers by writing both numbers as improper fractions and then subtracting. He wrote the following: $3\frac{3}{4} = \frac{15}{4}$ and $2\frac{5}{6} = \frac{17}{6}$. He then said that he needed to find a common denominator before he could subtract. His next step was:

$$3\frac{3}{4} = \frac{15 \cdot 3}{4 \cdot 3} = \frac{45}{12}$$

$$-2\frac{5}{6} = \frac{17 \cdot 2}{6 \cdot 2} = \frac{34}{12}$$

a) What did Ray get for his final answer?

b) Will Ray's improper fraction method always work? Try Ray's method for the following and compare the answers to answers found using another method of your choice (a number line, area model or only numbers).

- $\frac{11}{12} - \frac{5}{6}$

- $4\frac{1}{2} - 2\frac{3}{8}$

- $5\frac{1}{6} - 3\frac{5}{9}$

- $2\frac{3}{4} - \frac{7}{8}$

c) For a problem like $37\frac{1}{2} - 18\frac{2}{3}$, would you want to use Ray's improper fraction method? Why or why not?

8. Find the value of n that makes each number sentence true. Show your work.

a) $\frac{3}{8} + n = 2\frac{1}{4}$

b) $n = \frac{7}{9} - \frac{2}{3}$

c) $n - 2\frac{5}{9} = 7\frac{1}{3}$

9. Which of the following is correct? Correct each incorrect answer. Show your work.

a) $13\frac{1}{4} - 7\frac{3}{4} = 5\frac{1}{2}$

b) $7\frac{3}{4} - 4\frac{3}{8} = 3\frac{3}{8}$

c) $8\frac{3}{4} - 4\frac{5}{6} = 4\frac{1}{12}$

 **Think Beyond**

10. LaKeesha used the following negative numbers method to find the difference between $3\frac{1}{8}$ and $1\frac{3}{4}$:

$$
\begin{array}{r}
3 \quad \frac{1}{8} \\
- 1 \quad \frac{6}{8} \\
\hline
2 \quad -\frac{5}{8} = 1\frac{3}{8}
\end{array}
$$

Use LaKeesha's negative numbers method to find the following differences. Show your work.

a) $2\frac{3}{4} - \frac{5}{6}$ b) $3\frac{7}{12} - 2\frac{3}{4}$

Think Beyond

11. Identify two fractions with a sum of $1\frac{1}{8}$ and a difference of $\frac{3}{8}$.

12. What is the length of the toothpick?

13. A movie began at 11:45 am and ended at 1:20 pm. How long was the movie?

   a) Give the answer in hours and minutes.

   b) Give the answer in hours as a mixed number.

14. A number cube was rolled several times with the results shown on the following line plot.

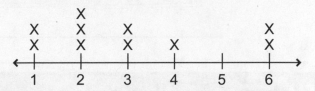

   a) How many times was the number cube rolled?

   b) What number was rolled most often?

   c) What fraction of the rolls were even numbers?

15. There are several socks in a drawer. Three are black, two are white, four are gray and five are navy. If you pull one sock out without looking:

   a) What is the probability that it is gray?

   b) What is the probability that it is not white?

16. Look at the following pattern.

   a) What percent of the square is shaded?

   b) What fractional part of the square is shaded?

   c) Write the unshaded portion of the square as a decimal.

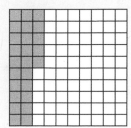

Start It Off

Mark bought two of the following and got $14.85 back in change from a twenty-dollar bill. There is no tax on food. Which two things did he buy? Explain your reasoning to a partner.

$3.89

$4.88

$1.26

$2.79

$3.42

CRACKERS

CEREAL

PEANUTS

Pretzels

WAFFLES

Archery

The next event in the mini-Olympiad was archery. For this contest, the class used rubber bands for bows and cotton balls for arrows. They decided to measure the distances the cotton balls traveled to the nearest hundredth of a meter. Each contestant was asked to predict the distance of their shot before actually trying it. Each student wrote the prediction on a class chart, shot the cotton ball and measured the distance.

Name	Prediction	Actual Distance
J.C.	1.2 m	4.03 m
Edwina	3.05 m	2.8 m
Amos	5.25 m	3.75 m
Judi	4 m	3.89 m
Benita	6.2 m	5.13 m
Emma	4.75 m	1.8 m

1. Use your estimation skills to list the students whose predictions were more than 1 meter different from the actual distances.

   a) Which students had predictions that were more than 2 meters different than the actual distances?

   b) Which student made the best prediction?

c) Discuss with a partner how to find the difference between the prediction and the actual distance for each of these students.

2. Show Edwina's prediction and actual distance on a number line.

   a) What is the difference between her prediction and her actual distance? How is this shown on the number line?

   b) Write Edwina's prediction and actual distance in centimeters. What is the difference between the two in centimeters? How does this compare to your answer in Part a?

3. Benita said that you can subtract decimals the same way you subtract whole numbers as long as they have the same number of decimal places. She used Amos's prediction and actual distance as an example.

   She wrote:

$$\begin{array}{r} 5.25 \\ -\ \ 3.75 \\ \hline \end{array}$$

   a) Find the difference the way you think that Benita might have completed this.

   b) Write Amos's distances as centimeters and find the difference. Compare this to your answer in Part a.

4. Ebbie says: $25 - 4.29 = 21.29$

   a) How might you explain her mistake using reasoning and estimation?

   b) How might you find the correct difference using an algorithm?

   c) Check your answer by converting 25 m and 4.29 m to centimeters and subtracting.

   d) Check your answer by subtracting $25.00 - $4.29.

   e) How do all these methods compare?

5. Find each difference using a method of your choice. Show your work.

   a) $12.60 - $4.30   **d)** $6.02 - 4.1$

   b) $4.1 - 2.9$ **e)** $5 - $3.67

   c) $5 - 2.3$ **f)** $3.02 - 2.675$

6. Make up your own subtraction problems using the cotton ball archery predictions and actual distances. Trade problems with a partner and compare answers.

· · · · · The Target Game · · · · ·

Players: 2 (or two teams of two players each)

Materials: Calculator

DIRECTIONS:

The first player names a number with at least two decimal places, and the second player puts this number in the calculator. The second player then names another number and hands the calculator back to the first player. The first player must add or subtract to get the second player's number to appear on the calculator. For example, the first player might say twenty-four and sixty-five hundredths. The second player puts 24.65 in the calculator and names a new number, thirty-two and four-tenths, for example. The first player has to add or subtract from 24.65 to get the calculator to show 32.4. Players must use mental computation. After each round, players switch roles.

Scoring: The first player gets three tries to get the new number. If this is done in one try, the first player gets 10 points. If it takes two tries, the first player gets 5 points. If it takes three tries, the first player gets 1 point. The player with the highest score at the end of the time is the winner.

 **rap It Up**

When subtracting decimals, you might convert them to fractions, you might use a model such as a number line or you might compute using an algorithm with decimals. Choose a number less than 10 with two decimal places and a number greater than 10 with one decimal place. Explain how you would find the difference between them using two methods of your choice.

LESSON
3.6

SECTION 3

On Your Own

MATERIALS LIST

▶ Lesson Guide 3.6:
  On Your Own

Write About It

1. Explain how you might find the difference between 4.375 and 2.75 using each of the following methods.

   a) Convert each decimal to a fraction, subtract the fractions and convert the answer back to a decimal.

   b) Show the difference on a number line.

   c) Use another method.

   d) Which method do you prefer for this problem? Why?

   e) Would you prefer to use the same method to subtract decimals in all problems or does it depend on the problem? Explain.

2. There are many ways to find the difference between two decimals. These are two that the class used to find the difference between the prediction of 5.25 meters and actual distance of 3.75 meters for Amos's shot.

   a) Amos changed his prediction and actual distance to fractions. He then computed $5\frac{1}{4} - 3\frac{3}{4}$. Use any method to find the difference between $5\frac{1}{4}$ and $3\frac{3}{4}$ using fractions.

   b) Edwina first thought 3.75 is 0.25 less than 4.0. From 4 to 5 is another 1 and from 5 to 5.25 is another 0.25. She then added to find the total. Use Edwina's method to determine if she got the same answer as Amos.

3. Estimate each of the following differences to the nearest whole or half meter. Use benchmarks of a whole or a half, but do not find the exact difference.

   a) 13.52 m − 4.984 m

   b) 12.24 m − 3.01 m

   c) 11.562 m − 4.4 m

4. Find n in each of the following. Show your work.

   a) $14.675 + n = 20$

   b) $n - 82.4 = 26.95$

   c) $n = 14.2 - 9.235$

5. The perimeter of the following quadrilateral is 40 meters. What is the missing length?

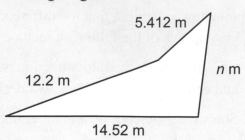

5.412 m

n m

12.2 m

14.52 m

6. The sum of the measures of the three angles of a triangle is 180 degrees. In the triangle below, the measures of two angles are shown. What is the measure of the third angle?

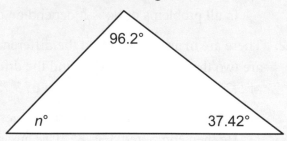

96.2°

n°

37.42°

7. Use the method of your choice to find each difference.

    a) $14 - 8.25 =$

    b) $12.34 - 7.8 =$

    c) $6.625 - 2.75 =$

    d) $4.05 - 2.673 =$

8. Ms. Jacobs spent $47.83 at the grocery store and gave the clerk three twenty-dollar bills. How much change should she have received? List the bills and coins the clerk might have given her as change.

9. When you subtract 3 dollars and 85 cents from 5 dollars and 25 cents, you can write this as $5.25 − $3.85. If you subtract 3 feet and 7 inches from 5 feet and 2 inches, can you write this as 5.2 − 3.7? Why or why not?

Think Beyond

10. Use the numbers 2, 3, 7 and 8 each once in the blanks in each problem to form true equations.

    a) $0.\underline{\hspace{1cm}}\ \underline{\hspace{1cm}} - 0.\underline{\hspace{1cm}}\ \underline{\hspace{1cm}} = 0.09$

    b) $6.5 - \underline{\hspace{1cm}}.\underline{\hspace{1cm}} = \underline{\hspace{1cm}}.\underline{\hspace{1cm}}$

    c) How many different ways can you answer Part b? Show them.

11. Tell whether each list is ordered from least to greatest. If the numbers are not in the correct order, order them.

   a) 3, 3.2, 3.14, 3.158

   b) 0.235, 2.035, 2.305, 2.350

   c) 4.5, 4.51, 4.154, 4.6

12. Place decimal points in 42 and 465 so the sum is 4.665.

13. Estimate each of the following sums to the nearest whole or half meter. Use benchmarks of a whole or half, but do not find the exact sum.

   a) 3.52 m + 14.984 m

   b) 12.024 m + 3.1 m

   c) 1.562 m + 4.4 m

14. Find the perimeter of the triangle.

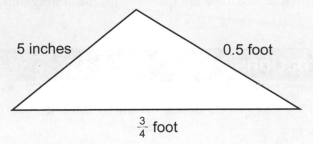

5 inches   0.5 foot

$\frac{3}{4}$ foot

15. How many boxes that each weigh 43 pounds would it take to have at least 1 ton?

Optional Technology Lesson for this section available in your eBook

Sum It Up

In this section, you investigated different methods for adding and subtracting fractions, decimals and mixed numbers. The following are some of the important ideas that you should have learned in this section.

- When adding and subtracting rational numbers, always estimate first to determine a reasonable answer. Check if your estimate and answer are close. In some cases, a reasonable estimate is all you need.

- A number line is an excellent model to use when adding and subtracting fractions and decimals.

- Money and metric measures are often useful for adding and subtracting decimals.

Adding Fractions

- Add fractions with different denominators by finding a common denominator.
  Example: $\frac{7}{8} + \frac{3}{5}$

$$\frac{7}{8} = \frac{7 \cdot 5}{8 \cdot 5} = \frac{35}{40}$$
$$+ \frac{3}{5} = \frac{3 \cdot 8}{5 \cdot 8} = \frac{24}{40}$$
$$\frac{59}{40} = 1\frac{19}{40}$$

- To add mixed numbers, the whole numbers and fractions can be added separately. Improper fractions in the sum should be changed to mixed numbers. For example, to add $3\frac{2}{3} + 4\frac{3}{5}$, you might write the following:

$$3\frac{2}{3} = 3\frac{2 \cdot 5}{3 \cdot 5} = 3\frac{10}{15}$$
$$+ 4\frac{3}{5} = 4\frac{3 \cdot 3}{5 \cdot 3} = 4\frac{9}{15}$$
$$7\frac{19}{15} = 8\frac{4}{15}$$

- Unit fractions have a numerator of 1. Egyptians knew that every unit fraction could be written as the sum of two or more different fractions. For example: $\frac{1}{2} = \frac{1}{3} + \frac{1}{6}$

- In magic squares, the sum of each row, column and diagonal is the same. Magic squares can consist of any rational numbers, including fractions and decimals. For example, the following square has a magic sum of $1\frac{1}{2}$ for each row, column and diagonal.

$\frac{1}{6}$	$\frac{7}{9}$	$\frac{5}{9}$
$\frac{8}{9}$	$\frac{1}{2}$	$\frac{1}{9}$
$\frac{4}{9}$	$\frac{2}{9}$	$\frac{5}{6}$

Adding Decimals

- Fractions can be converted to decimal equivalents and then added.

- You can write decimals in a column in which the decimal points are lined up. If the numbers have a different number of decimal places, you should first write them as equivalent decimals with the same number of decimal places. For example, to add $3.2 + 4.35 + 18.234$, first write each as an equivalent number of thousandths.

This can be written as:

$$
\begin{array}{r}
3.200 \\
4.350 \\
+\ 18.234 \\
\hline
25.784
\end{array}
$$

- Decimals can be converted to fractions or mixed numbers and then added. For example, to add $3.2 + 4.35$, you might write this as $3\frac{20}{100} + 4\frac{35}{100} = 7\frac{55}{100} = 7.55$.

Subtracting Fractions and Decimals

- There are many ways to subtract rational numbers. To subtract rational numbers in fraction form, write them as equivalent fractions with a common denominator and subtract the numerators. For example, to subtract $\frac{7}{8} - \frac{3}{4}$, first write both with a common denominator, which in this case might be eighths.

$$
\begin{array}{r}
\frac{7}{8} = \frac{7}{8} \\
-\ \frac{3}{4} = \frac{6}{8} \\
\hline
\frac{1}{8}
\end{array}
$$

7 eighths − 6 eighths = 1 eighth

- When subtracting mixed numbers, if the fraction portion of the minuend (the first number) is larger than the fraction portion of the subtrahend (the second number), you can subtract the whole numbers and then subtract the fraction portions. If the fraction in the subtrahend is larger, you can regroup one whole in the minuend to create an improper fraction and then subtract after finding a common denominator. For example, to subtract $4\frac{1}{3} - 2\frac{1}{2}$, you might write:

$$
\begin{aligned}
4\tfrac{1}{3} = 3\tfrac{4}{3} &= 3\tfrac{8}{6} \\
-\qquad 2\tfrac{1}{2} &= 2\tfrac{3}{6} \\
\hline
&\ \ 1\tfrac{5}{6}
\end{aligned}
$$

- You can also subtract mixed numbers by adding up. For example, to subtract $4\frac{1}{3} - 2\frac{1}{2}$ you might think, $2\frac{1}{2} + \frac{1}{2}$. Then you could think $3 + 1\frac{1}{3} = 4\frac{1}{3}$. You would then add $\frac{1}{2} + 1\frac{1}{3} = \frac{3}{6} + 1\frac{2}{6} = 1\frac{5}{6}$. You can see this process on a number line.

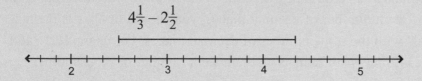

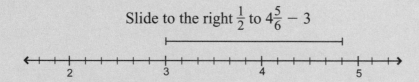

Slide to the right $\frac{1}{2}$ to $4\frac{5}{6} - 3$

- You can subtract decimals by first rewriting them as fractions or by leaving the numbers in decimal form. As with addition, it is important to make sure that the decimal points are lined up. If the numbers have a different number of decimal places, they should first be written as equivalent decimals with the same number of places. For example, to subtract $13.2 - 9.876$, you might write:

$$
\begin{array}{r}
13.200 \\
-\ 9.875 \\
\hline
3.325
\end{array}
$$

Study Guide

Addition and Subtraction of Fractions and Decimals

Part 1. What did you learn?

1. Compute. Show your work.

   a. $3\frac{1}{4} + 2\frac{3}{8}$

   b. $6\frac{1}{8} - 3\frac{1}{4}$

   c. $10\frac{1}{2} + 7.24$

   d. $2.3 + 2.63$

   e. $7 - 5.07$

2. Compute $5 - 3\frac{3}{4}$ first by adding up and then by using regrouping. Show your work.

3. Use what you have learned about the adding up method to match each expression in Column I with the equivalent expression in Column II and the correct difference in Column III.

Column I	Column II	Column III
a. $6 - 1\frac{7}{8}$	e. $4\frac{1}{2} - 2$	i. $4\frac{1}{4}$
b. $4\frac{1}{4} - 1\frac{3}{4}$	f. $4\frac{3}{4} - 2$	j. $4\frac{1}{8}$
c. $6 - 1\frac{3}{4}$	g. $6\frac{1}{8} - 2$	k. $2\frac{3}{4}$
d. $4\frac{1}{4} - 1\frac{1}{2}$	h. $6\frac{1}{4} - 2$	l. $2\frac{1}{2}$

4. Nina spends one-twentieth of an hour tuning her guitar, one-fourth of an hour practicing scales, three-fifths of an hour sight-reading music, and three-fourths of an hour practicing her upcoming concert pieces.

   a. How many hours does Nina play her guitar? Write your answer as a mixed number.

   b. Write your answer from Part a in hours and minutes.

5. Jorge participates in three sports during the week: soccer, basketball and hockey. He spends a total of $5\frac{3}{4}$ hours playing all three sports each week. How much time might Jorge spend playing *each* sport? Show or explain how you got your answer.

6. Find two fractions with a sum that is greater than $\frac{3}{4}$ and less than $\frac{15}{16}$. Write your fractions in simplest form and find the actual sum.

7. Find two fractions with a sum that is greater than 1.6 but less than 1.9. Write your fractions in simplest form and compute their exact sum.

8. Copy and complete the magic square using fractions in simplest form. The magic sum is $\frac{5}{6}$.

	$\frac{5}{18}$	
$\frac{1}{3}$		$\frac{1}{9}$

9. Find *n* in each of the following equations.

   a. $0.32 = 0.05 + 0.25 + n$

   b. $0.2 + 0.45 = n + 0.51$

   c. $0.01 + n = 0.04 + 0.06$

10. Scott is preparing to run a 5K—a race that is 5 kilometers long. He ran 1.3 km on Monday, 2.2 km on Tuesday, 0.8 km on Wednesday, and 1.45 km on Thursday. How many kilometers did he run in total from Monday through Thursday?

11. Yajahira is also training to run a 5K. She ran Monday through Thursday for a total of 6.5 kilometers. How far might she have run each day? Show or explain how you got your answer.

12. Use the Student Trail Mix Ingredients from page 110 to answer these questions.

   a. Maria mixed almonds, M&M's® and banana chips. How much trail mix did she make with these three ingredients? Show or explain how you got your answer.

   b. Choose four ingredients that could be mixed to make between 1 and $1\frac{1}{2}$ kg of trail mix. Show or explain how you got your answer.

   c. John mixed chocolate chips, coconut, sesame sticks and M&M's®. Which ingredient could he add to make exactly 1 kg of trail mix? Show or explain how you got your answer.

13. JoEllen bought fabric to make her costume for the school play. She made a pair of pants and a shirt with the fabric. She bought a total of $5\frac{3}{4}$ yards of fabric. She used $2\frac{7}{8}$ for the shirt and the rest for the pants. How much fabric did JoEllen use to make the pants?

14. Klarka and Kimmi participated in the straw javelin throw. They observed that their distances were $2\frac{1}{6}$ feet apart. What might have been each girl's distance?

15. Deena was asked to compute $6\frac{1}{4} - 4\frac{5}{8}$ on a recent quiz. Her work is shown below.

$$6\frac{1}{4} = \overset{5}{\cancel{6}}\,\overset{8}{\underset{8}{\cancel{2}}}$$
$$-4\frac{5}{8} \qquad -4\frac{5}{8}$$
$$\boxed{1\frac{3}{8}}$$

Deena's answer was marked wrong. Why? What could you say or do to help Deena find the correct answer to this computation?

16. Jeffrey was asked to compute $2.53 - 1.46$ on a recent quiz. His work is shown below.

$$\begin{array}{r} 2.53 \\ -\ 1.46 \\ \hline 1.13 \end{array}$$

Jeffrey's answer was marked wrong. Why? What could you say or do to help Jeffrey find the correct answer to this computation?

Unit Study Guide

Notable Numbers:
Focusing on Fractions,
Decimals and Percents

MATERIALS LIST

▶ Ruler

Part 1. What did you learn?

SECTION 1

1. Put the following rational numbers in order from least to greatest.

   $\frac{2}{3}$, 4, 12.5%, 1.25, 4%

2. Delano's Pizza Place kept track of the numbers and types of pizzas ordered on one Saturday night. They organized the results in the pie chart below and made the following notes: $\frac{1}{5}$ of the people ordered pepperoni pizza, 0.45 ordered cheese, 3 out of every 10 people ordered mushroom and the rest ordered olive pizza. Find the percent of orders for each type of pizza.

   Type of Pizza

   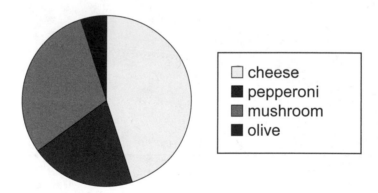

   ☐ cheese
   ■ pepperoni
   ■ mushroom
   ■ olive

3. If each small triangle represents $\frac{1}{4}$, write the value of the design below as a fraction, decimal and percent.

   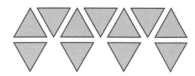

4. The small square is $\frac{1}{3}$ of the entire figure. What portion of the entire figure is the largest triangle?

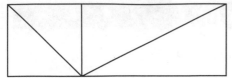

5. Copy and complete the following chart.

	Decimeters	Centimeters	Meters
45% of a meter			
$\frac{25}{10}$ cm			
$\frac{5}{4}$ m			

6. Determine which letter is closest to each of the rational numbers listed below.

   i. 0.475

   ii. 75%

   iii. 1.078

   iv. $\frac{20}{9}$

   v. 2.12

7. Find the least common denominator for each pair of fractions.

   a. $\frac{7}{8}, \frac{5}{6}$

   b. $\frac{1}{3}, \frac{5}{12}$

   c. $\frac{4}{5}, \frac{3}{4}$

   d. $\frac{2}{3}, \frac{4}{36}$

8. Write each fraction in simplest form.

   a. $\frac{16}{18}$

   b. $\frac{20}{6}$

   c. $\frac{120}{160}$

9. Use your inch ruler to measure the length of each of the following pictures to the nearest eighth of an inch.

   a.

   b.

10. Use your centimeter ruler to draw line segments with each of the following lengths:

    a. 2.5 decimeters

    b. 2.5 centimeters

    c. 20.5% of a meter

11. Use at least two different methods (common denominator, common numerator, compare to 0, $\frac{1}{2}$ or 1, and compare missing parts) to compare each pair of fractions. Show your work.

    a. $\frac{7}{8}$ and $\frac{8}{9}$

    b. $\frac{3}{7}$ and $\frac{4}{9}$

    c. $\frac{12}{7}$ and $\frac{6}{5}$

    d. $\frac{3}{4}$ and $\frac{5}{12}$

12. Adair is a carpenter. She needs pieces of lumber of varying thickness for a bookcase she is building. The piece of lumber for the back of the bookcase is $\frac{7}{8}$ inch thick. The piece of lumber for each side of the bookcase is $\frac{15}{16}$ inch thick. The piece of lumber for each shelf is $\frac{3}{4}$ inch thick.

    a. Order the pieces by thickness, from least to greatest thickness. Show your work.

    b. Adair needs to buy another piece of lumber for the top shelf. She wants the top shelf to be thicker than the other shelves but not as thick as 1 inch. What thickness might she use for the top shelf? Show or explain how you got your answer.

13. In a recent swim meet, the winner's time was 60.41 seconds and the time of the third place finisher was 60.42 seconds. What might have been the time of the second place finisher?

14. For her science class, Mare had to keep track of a plant's growth over time. Mare's teacher encouraged her to be as precise as possible with her measurements. By the 14th week, Mare used an inch ruler and found that her plant was greater than $6\frac{7}{8}$ inches but less than $6\frac{15}{16}$ inches. What might Mare report for her plant's height?

15. Express each sum or difference as (i) a fraction in simplest form (ii) a decimal and (iii) a percent.

    a. The part of a dollar that is equal to 65% of a dollar plus $\frac{1}{25}$ of a dollar

    b. The part of a meter that is equal to 12 cm less than 0.4 meter

    c. The part of an hour that is equal to $\frac{2}{5}$ of an hour plus 0.1 of an hour

16. Complete the conversions listed in the chart below.

	Decimeters	Centimeters	Meters
a. 2 cm more than 45% of a meter			
b. $\frac{25}{10}$ cm + 0.05 m			
c. 4.4 dm + 2 cm + 100% of a meter			
d. $\frac{5}{4}$ meter + 20% of a meter			

17. Solve for n. Write your answers in simplest terms.

    a. $\frac{12}{16} + \frac{1}{4} = n + \frac{3}{16}$

    b. $\frac{20}{18} + \frac{1}{3} = n + \frac{2}{9}$

18. Each expression below describes a rational number. Determine which letter on the number line below is closest to each rational number described.

    i. four hundredths more than 30.9

    ii. six hundredths less than 30.04

    iii. three tenths more than 30.85

    iv. forty-two hundredths more than 31.22

    v. seven tenths less than 31.15

19. Blake is making fruit punch using $\frac{3}{8}$ quart of cherry juice, 0.5 quart of apple juice, and $\frac{1}{4}$ quart of strawberry juice. Does she have enough juice to make 1 quart of fruit punch? Why or why not?

20. In the mini-Olympics, Ted threw the paper plate discus $3\frac{1}{6}$ feet and Ursula threw it $4\frac{7}{8}$ feet. How much farther did Ursula throw the discus than Ted? Use two different methods (mental math, number line or an algorithm) to find the answer.

21. The perimeter of the following triangle is 30 cm. What is the missing length?

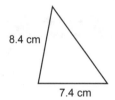

8.4 cm

7.4 cm

22. Match each expression in Column A with the best estimate of its sum or difference in Column B.

	Expression		Estimate
a.	$\frac{1}{9} + \frac{2}{5} + \frac{9}{10}$	**e.**	$\frac{4}{5}$
b.	$\frac{1}{4} + \frac{1}{2} + \frac{9}{16}$	**f.**	1
c.	$3\frac{4}{5} - 2\frac{9}{10}$	**g.**	$1\frac{2}{5}$
d.	$7\frac{1}{2} - 6\frac{4}{9}$	**h.**	$1\frac{1}{4}$

23. Compute. Show your work.

a. $2\frac{5}{6} + 4\frac{3}{5}$

b. $2\frac{2}{3} + 4\frac{4}{5}$

c. $1\frac{1}{4} - \frac{7}{12}$

d. $12\frac{3}{4} - 9\frac{5}{6}$

e. $7.43 + 23.9$

f. $6.34 - 2.61$

24. Santiago wants to try the "adding on" method for subtracting mixed numbers, but he is confused about when he should use it. Would you recommend that Santiago use this algorithm for either Part c or d in question 23 on page 142? Why or why not?

Part 2. What went wrong?

25. Jake added $0.7 + 0.35$ using the following steps:

$$0.7 + 0.35 = \frac{0.7}{10} + \frac{0.35}{100} = \frac{7.0}{100} + \frac{0.35}{100} = \frac{7.35}{100}$$

Jake's friend Jocelyn said, "That can't be right. The sum should be around 1." Do you agree with Jocelyn's estimate? If so, what is wrong with Jake's method?

26. Gideon was asked the following question on a recent quiz:

What is 2.25 minutes written as minutes and seconds?

A. 2 min. and 25 sec.   C. 2 min. and 15 sec.

B. 2 min. and 30 sec.   D. 2 min. and $\frac{1}{4}$ sec.

Gideon chose answer A, but it was marked wrong. What is the correct answer? What could you do or say to help Gideon make sense of the correct answer?

27. Ravello was asked to compute $12\frac{1}{8} - 8\frac{3}{4}$. His work is shown below.

$$
\begin{array}{rcr}
12\frac{1}{8} & = & 12\frac{1}{8} \\
- \ 8\frac{3}{4} & = & - \ 8\frac{6}{8} \\
\hline
& & 4\frac{5}{8}
\end{array}
$$

Ravello's answer was marked wrong. Why? What could you say or do to help Ravello find the correct answer to this computation?

Glossary

algorithm A set of step-by-step instructions or procedures used to solve a problem.

Example:
Algorithm to find the least common denominator of two fractions:

1. List the first ten multiples of each denominator.

2. Identify the smallest multiple that appears on both lists. If no multiples are the same, list the next five multiples of each denominator and repeat step 2.

3. This multiple is the least common multiple of the two numbers and therefore the least common denominator of the two fractions.

---

annex zero To add a zero after the last digit to the right of the decimal point.

Example:
To find equivalent decimals, we can annex zeros beyond the last decimal place.

0.4 is equivalent to 0.40 and 0.400.

254.45 is equivalent to 254.45000.

---

benchmark A point with a known value used as a reference to determine the magnitude and direction of another point or to order a list of numbers.

Example:
When ordering the fractions $\frac{1}{8}$, $\frac{5}{12}$, $\frac{9}{16}$ and $\frac{6}{7}$ from least to greatest, use the benchmarks of 0, $\frac{1}{2}$ and 1. Note that:

$\frac{5}{12} < \frac{6}{12} = \frac{1}{2}$ and $\frac{9}{16} > \frac{8}{16} = \frac{1}{2}$, so $\frac{5}{12} < \frac{9}{16}$.

$\frac{1}{8}$ is close to 0 and $\frac{6}{7}$ is close to 1.

The order is $\frac{1}{8}$, $\frac{5}{12}$, $\frac{9}{16}$, $\frac{6}{7}$.

---

circle graph (pie chart) A display of data in the form of a circle divided into proportionally sized sections (pie slices).

Example:
Of 30 students surveyed, the following pie chart reflects their favorite meal of the day.

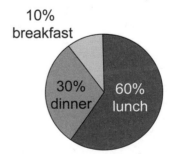

---

common denominator A whole number that is the denominator for all of a group of fractions.

Example:
Given the fractions $\frac{1}{8}$, $\frac{3}{4}$, $\frac{15}{8}$, $\frac{1}{2}$, and $\frac{12}{4}$, we can write the following equivalent fractions with a common denominator of 8:

$\frac{1}{8}$, $\frac{6}{8}$, $\frac{15}{8}$, $\frac{4}{8}$, $\frac{24}{8}$.

common fraction A fraction where the numerator and denominator are both integers.

Example:

$$\frac{2}{3}, \frac{5}{12}, \frac{9}{4}, \frac{8}{16}, \frac{7}{2}$$

---

decimal A number represented in the base-10 place-value system.

Example:

678, 45.67, 34.0500, 0.93

---

decimal place The position of a digit to the right of the decimal point.

Example:

The decimal 12.345 has three decimal places.

$\frac{1}{6} = 0.1666 \ldots$ and rounded to two decimal places is 0.17.

In the decimal 0.25, the digit 2 is in the first decimal place.

---

denominator The bottom number in the fraction representation of a number.

Example:

In $\frac{8}{9}$, the denominator is 9.

In $\frac{5}{3}$, the denominator is 3.

---

divisor (in a division problem) The number that is doing the dividing in a division problem.

Example:

The following are forms of the division problem "twenty-three divided by five."

The number 5 is the divisor.

$$23 \div 5 = 4.6$$
$$\frac{23}{5} = 4.6$$
$$\begin{array}{r} 4\ R3 \\ 5\overline{)23} \end{array}$$

---

divisor (as a factor of a number) Another name for a factor of a given number. The given number is said to be "divisible by" its factors/divisors.

Example:

The number 8 is divisible by its factors: 1, 2, 4 and 8.

$$8 \div 1 = 8 \qquad 8 \div 2 = 4$$
$$8 \div 4 = 2 \qquad 8 \div 8 = 1$$

Therefore, 1, 2, 4, and 8 are divisors of 8.

---

equivalent decimals Different decimal representations of the same number.

Example:

$$0.3 = 0.30 = 0.300$$
$$1.579 = 1.5790 = 1.57900$$

---

equivalent fractions Different fraction representations of the same number (equal values, but different numerators and denominators).

Example:

$$\frac{1}{2} = \frac{2}{4} = \frac{20}{40} = \frac{120}{240}$$
$$\frac{3}{9} = \frac{6}{18} = \frac{9}{27} = \frac{300}{900}$$

factor (of a number) A positive integer that, when multiplied by another positive integer, results in the given number. Therefore, the quotient of the number and the factor will have no remainder.

Example:
The factors of 10 are 1, 2, 5 and 10.

The factors of 64 are 1, 2, 4, 8, 16, 32 and 64.

---

fraction An expression indicating the quotient of two quantities. A quotient in the form $\frac{a}{b}$ read as "a over b."

Example:
$\frac{4}{5}$ is the fraction "four-fifths" or "four over five."

---

gram A metric unit for mass.

Example:
1,000 grams = 1 kilogram

1 gram $\approx$ 0.0022 pound

---

greatest common divisor (GCD) The greatest (largest) whole number that divides evenly into two or more numbers. Also known as the greatest common factor.

Example:
The divisors of 20 are 1, 2, 4, 5, 10 and 20.

The divisors of 50 are 1, 2, 5, 10, 25 and 50.

The GCD of 20 and 50 is 10.

---

greatest common factor (GCF) The greatest (largest) factor of two or more numbers. Also known as the greatest common divisor.

Example:
The factors of 20 are 1, 2, 4, 5, 10 and 20.

The factors of 50 are 1, 2, 5, 10, 25 and 50.

The GCF of 20 and 50 is 10.

---

improper fraction A fraction in which the numerator is greater than (or equal to) the denominator.

Example:
$\frac{4}{3}, \frac{8}{2}, \frac{51}{37}, \frac{150}{9}, \frac{1,290}{4}, \frac{3}{3}$

---

integers The set of whole numbers and their opposites (the negative of each whole number) $\{...\,^{-}3,\,^{-}2,\,^{-}1,\,0,\,1,\,2,\,3,\,...\}$.

---

least common denominator (LCD) The least (smallest) common multiple (LCM) of the denominators of two or more fractions.

Example:
The LCD of $\frac{1}{2}, \frac{2}{3}$ and $\frac{3}{5}$ is 30.

The equivalent fractions are $\frac{15}{30}, \frac{20}{30}$ and $\frac{18}{30}$.

---

least common multiple (LCM) The least (smallest) of the multiples that a group of numbers have in common.

Example:
The LCM of 2, 3 and 5 is 30.

2   2, 4, 6, 8, 10, ... 26, 28, <u>30</u>, ...

3   3, 6, 9, 12, 15,18, ... 24, 27, <u>30</u>, ...

5   5, 10, 15, 20, 25, <u>30</u>, ...

line plot (dot plot) A graph that shows along a number line how often values occur in a data set. Line plots are used to graph small sets of data.

Example:
Set C: {1, 2, 6, 4, 2, 3, 2, 4}

The line plot for Set C is:

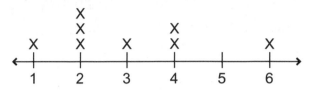

liter A metric measure for volume.

Example:
1 liter = 1,000 milliliters

1 liter ≈ 0.2642 gallon

magic square A square array of numbers in which the sum of the numbers in each row, column and diagonal is the same.

Example:
The magic sum of the following magic square is 15:

8	3	4
1	5	9
6	7	2

magic triangle A triangle array of numbers in which the sum of the numbers along each side of the triangle is the same.

Example:
The magic sum of the following magic triangle is 10:

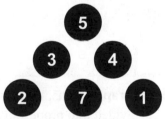

meter A metric unit for measuring length.

Example:
1 meter = 100 centimeters

1 meter ≈ 1.0936133 yards

minuend The number from which another number is subtracted in a difference problem.

Example:
minuend − subtrahend = difference

In 8 − 5 = 3, the minuend is 8.

mixed number (or numeral) A number greater than 1 written as a whole number and a fraction.

Example:
$1\frac{5}{8}$, $4\frac{2}{5}$, $99\frac{1}{9}$, $234\frac{5}{6}$

multiple The product of a given whole number and an integer.

Example:

10 is a multiple of 2 since $2 \times 5 = 10$.

27 is a multiple of 9 since $9 \times 3 = 27$.

numerator The top number in the fraction representation of a number.

Example:

In $\frac{8}{9}$, the numerator is 8.

In $\frac{5}{3}$, the numerator is 5.

percent A number expressed in relationship to 100 or "per hundred."

Example:

98% represents 98 per 100 or $\frac{98}{100}$.

24% represents 24 per 100 or 0.24.

percent circle A circle graph that is divided into 100 equal sections.

Example:

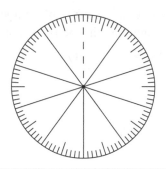

percent strip A ruler-like measuring tool whose length represents 100% and gradations represent proportional percent values.

Example:

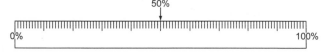

$\frac{1}{2}$ of the percent strip represents 50%.

pie chart (circle graph) A display of data in the form of a circle divided into proportionally-sized sections (pie slices).

Example:

Of 30 students surveyed, the following pie chart reflects their favorite meal of the day.

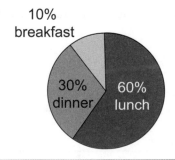

proper fraction A fraction representation of a number greater than 0 and less than 1. The numerator of the fraction is less than the denominator.

Example:

$\frac{1}{3}, \frac{4}{5}, \frac{97}{100}, \frac{1,244}{1,245}$

rational number A number that can be written as $\frac{a}{b}$ where a and b are integers and b does not equal 0.

Example:

$-2 = -\frac{2}{1}$, $4.5 = \frac{45}{10}$, $10.98765 = \frac{1,098,765}{100,000}$, $\frac{91}{99}$

---

simplest form (of a fraction) The fraction representation of a number in which the numerator and denominator have no common factors other than 1.

Example:

Simplest form: $\frac{1}{2}$, $\frac{2}{3}$, $\frac{99}{100}$, $\frac{9}{8}$.

Not in simplest form: $\frac{4}{8}$, $\frac{27}{81}$, $\frac{124}{200}$.

---

simplify (a fraction) The process of successively dividing the numerator and denominator of a fraction by common factors until the fraction is in simplest form.

Example:

Simplify $\frac{120}{200}$ by dividing both the numerator and denominator by 20 and then by 2.

$\frac{120}{200} = \frac{6}{10}$

$\frac{6}{10} = \frac{3}{5}$

---

subtrahend The number being subtracted in a difference problem.

Example:

minuend $-$ subtrahend $=$ difference

In $8 - 5 = 3$, the subtrahend is 5.

---

unit fraction A fraction whose numerator is 1.

Example:

$\frac{1}{2}$, $\frac{1}{3}$, $\frac{1}{10}$, $\frac{1}{89}$

---

whole number The set of counting numbers and zero $\{0, 1, 2, 3, 4, \dots\}$.

Lesson 1.1

Percent Strips
Page 4, Question 7d: Where is 1% on your percent strip?

Lesson 1.5

On Your Own
Page 39 , Question 11:
8 ounces = 1 cup
1 gallon = 16 cups

Lesson 1.7

On Your Own
Page 50, Question 5c: What is the new total number of fish in the pond?

Lesson 2.3

Fractions in the Middle
Page 72, Question 1b: Try renaming each fraction using another denominator.

Lesson 3.1

Asia
Page 97, Question 3b: 36 inches = 1 yard

Lesson 3.2

Worldwide Magic
Page 97: Look at the total number of dots in each row, column, or diagonal.

On Your Own
Page 99, Question 1: What happens if you multiply or divide every number in this square by the same number?

Index